C0-AZX-448

Upstream, Downstream AND *Out Of My Mind*

Other Books by SYD HOFF

FEELING NO PAIN
OOPS, WRONG STATEROOM!
OOPS, WRONG PARTY!
MOM, I'M HOME
OUT OF GAS
OKAY, YOU CAN LOOK NOW
DANNY AND THE DINOSAUR

Upstream, Downstream AND *Out Of My Mind*

by SYD HOFF

THE BOBBS-MERRILL COMPANY, INC.
A SUBSIDIARY OF HOWARD W. SAMS & CO., INC.
Publishers • INDIANAPOLIS • NEW YORK

Printed in the United States of America

First Edition

Library of Congress Catalog Card No.: 61-7909

For

THE WORM, WHO MIGHT OTHERWISE
FEEL NEGLECTED BY ALL THIS

All in the fragrant Prime of day,
Ere Phoebus spreads around his beams,
The early Angler takes his way
To verdant banks of crystal stream.
If health, content, and thoughtful musing charm,
What sport like angling can our cares disarm?

Upstream, Downstream AND *Out Of My Mind*

1

WHEN I first announced to a waiting world that I was considering going in for fly casting, large numbers of my friends started casting—doubts on my wisdom.

"Oh, my God!" said one.

"I can just picture you," said another.

"Get the net," said a few others.

The sum total of these unsolicited opinions was that I could do better with a fly swatter than I could with a fly rod.

Actually I could hardly blame my friends for being skeptical. Was I not just a child of the metropolis, a son-of-the-sidewalks, trained only to stop and go on traffic lights? What entitled me to piscatorial illusions? True I had been to the aquarium several times, but . . .

I became known in our little set as the lunatic with a hankering for the sylvan glen and the babbling brook.

"Have you ever heard the maddening sound of a leaf falling?" my critics asked.

No, I had not.

"Have you ever been out in the Great Alone, and we don't mean a voting booth?" they hammered away.

The jury was hardly out a minute.

Verdict? Stay home.

And that was that. I put trout fishing out of my mind. You see, that's one of my troubles—I discourage too easily. If I had been Robert Fulton, I would have stayed in port when people started laughing. If I had been Romeo, I would have looked for another girl the minute Juliet's family didn't give me their approval. A few friends can talk me out of almost anything. Even a few strangers.

So the subject was forgotten and things ran along the same exciting way until one evening my wife interrupted me in the middle of a yawn.

"Why don't you go in for angling?" she asked.

"Why are you re-opening an old wound?" I cried out in anguish.

"Because there's a sale on fishing jackets in the department stores," she said, holding up the paper.

Maybe that was reason enough. I once heard of a man who bought a horse because someone gave him a lotion for saddle sores.

Anyway, the next thing I knew, my wife was reading to me from the Encyclopaedia Britannica.

"It says here, quote," she said, "it is among the most ancient of human activities and may be said to date from the time when man was in the infancy of the stone age, unquote."

"What is?" I asked.

"Angling," she answered.

"Now dear, just because I'm a caveman with you sometimes does not necessarily mean I'd make an angler," I argued.

"Nonsense," she retorted. "I think you'd make a very

good angler! In fact, I never knew anybody with more angles . . ."

Did Dora have an angle of her own? Women usually do.

"But high rubber boots, and all that," I said. "Do you think I'd look manly enough?"

"Why not?"

"I'm thinking of how Calvin Coolidge used to look in the newsreels long ago."

"He looked relaxed."

"He looked dead."

"He even looked that way as an Indian," she said, to close the subject.

The following day I went to the doctor for a checkup. I go regularly of late—whenever I see a friend's name in the obituary columns.

"You've been overworking," he said, taking off his stethoscope.

I felt faint and leaned against his blonde nurse. Or maybe I didn't feel faint at all.

"Where does it show, Doc?" I asked.

"Right here," he laughed, tapping me on the money belt.

I smiled at his sally, and also at his Irene—which happened to be the nurse's name.

"Lately I'm telling everbody the same thing," he said. "Go fishing."

"Why?" I asked.

"So there'll be more room on the golf courses," he replied, taking a practice swing with his putter.

Following that I went to see another custodian of my health—my accountant.

"Don't take them off yet, George. There's a leak in the basement."

"You've been overworking," he said.

There was no nurse to lean against.

"How can you tell?" I asked.

"You've just entered a higher income tax bracket," he chuckled.

"You don't have to sound so elated about it," I complained.

"Lately I'm telling everybody the same thing," he began.

"I know—go fishing!" I said, tripping over his golf bag on the way out.

I took other tests . . .

Then I went home.

Was it Fate that conspired to get the long-handled bath brush all tangled up with the dental floss? Anyway, when I glanced up at the mirror over the wash basin, I beheld a boy fishing—a boy with balding head but nevertheless, a boy . . .

"What a fool you've been!" I cried aloud to the image, and went running for the encyclopedia.

After apologizing to ANGLIN, MARGARET (1876-) American actress, for my appearance, I started soaking up information on ANGLING.

For instance, I learned that those stone age men didn't merely go around pulling girls by their hair but took time out to go fishing and even invented some fish hooks, that a Greek writer named Plutarch once wrote about a fishing contest between Antony and Cleopatra (a fact that had been concealed from me—I thought they only went in for indoor sports), that Izaak Walton's *The Compleat Angler* was a best seller in 1653 way before The Book of the Month

"Those spots you keep seeing—are they dry flies or wet flies?"

Club, and that a naturalist named Johnson discovered in 1904 how to tell the age of a salmon by counting its scales—which must have made a lot of lady salmon very angry.

I also touched on Fish Culture, Methods and Practice, and Fresh Water Fishing, before finally pulling out the stopper.

After dressing I read further on angling. Then I looked up Trout in another volume, and found out that it is "closely related to the salmon, but with a larger mouth," and that "midwestern restaurants sometimes serve catfish under the name of trout"—which made me wonder about some excellent trout dinners I had enjoyed in the past.

Now the passion was in me. I must meet a trout—get to know one personally!

> Man, forty-ish, educated, fond of music,
> good books, theatre, would like to
> hear from trout. . . .

That would do no good. Trout don't read. Or were there book trout, as well as brook trout?

I looked up Fishing Tackle Shops in the yellow pages, made a selection, and having an hour or so before I was to meet my wife for dinner, went there at once.

The adventure was begun!

2

As I entered HARRY'S FISHIN' HOLE, BIG DISCOUNTS, LIVE BAIT, TACKLE, FREE INFORMATION, I affected a rolling gait. Or was it just sailors that had rolling gaits, I tried to remember, and not fishermen? I felt as nervous as the bridegroom in a lingerie shoppe, but I was going to try not to show it. Let Harry find out for himself!

"Poles," I said casually.

"Clothes or totem?" the man asked. He must have been Harry.

"I thought this was a fishing store."

"Tackle shops carry everything—motor cycles, carpet sweepers . . ."

"I want to fish," I said.

"Rods over there," he gestured.

I picked up one and ran it back and forth beween the second and third fingers of my left hand.

"You handle that pretty good, if you're going to shoot pool with it," observed Harry.

The blood rushed to my cheeks and I checked an impulse to challenge him to a fast game of Chicago or Rotation. Then coolness prevailed and I decided that perhaps it would be wiser to throw myself on his mercy.

"I'm new at this," I confessed, hanging my head.

"Never fished before, eh?"

"I tried it once, deep sea. But I got sick. I don't even remember what happened, except that everybody on the boat ate my lunch."

"And now you're going back?"

"No, let them bring their own lunch. I'm going to try trout fishing—fly casting."

Harry took the rod I was holding out of my hand.

"Well, well, well," he said. "Three wells make a river. What you want is a fly rod. I can sell you a cheap one, but you'd be a fool to buy it."

"Why?"

"It's like buying a car. You want something that'll stand a lot of use. Know how many times you'll be casting in an hour? About five hundred times. In a six-hour day, that's 3,000 castings. In one month it adds up to 90,000 casts."

"Ninety thousand and one, counting the cast I'll have on my arm," I said wryly.

Harry selected a rod. "Here's one. Eight feet—four ounces. Very popular."

"Sounds good."

"On a windy day, though, you'll need something heavier. This one's nine feet—five ounces."

"I better take both, don't you think?"

"You like lancewood, greenheart, glass fiber or bamboo?"

"What's the difference?"

"They're all good."

"Then I'll take one of each."

"How about reels? You like automatic or standards?"

I waited for him to elaborate.

"Automatic takes up line the second you need it."

"That's a point in its favor."

"However, some folks claim they're too heavy to balance."

"Why don't I take them both, just to make sure?"

"American make?"

"Buy American, I always say."

"They get jammed. English don't."

"Give me English then. No, wait a minute. Better make it American too. I don't want to have to hide my head whenever I pass the Mt. Rushmore Memorial."

"Now the line," Harry said. "You like nylon or silk?"

"On ladies' legs, either," I answered. "Which do you recommend?"

"They're about equal."

I flipped a coin and took nylon. While the coin was coming down, Harry sold me a collapsible drying reel, a snake-bite kit, a bottle of fish scent and an aluminum canoe.

"What do you like in leaders?" he asked.

"Either Democrat or Republican," I said.

"Silkworm doesn't have the strength of nylon."

"Then it's nylon."

"Trouble is sometimes nylon gets all knotted up, and there can be trouble submerging it."

"All right—silkworm."

"Now for flies. What do you like?"

What could I say? The only kind of flies I knew were the kind Willy Mays catches.

"I like a No. 12 Adam and a Light Cahill Quill," Harry said.

"Fine. I'll take a pound of each."

"I was about to tell you of some nice trout I've caught with a No. 20 Blue Upright, and a No. 12 Royal Coachman."

How could they tell what a trout would take?

"I haven't got time to listen now," I said. "Just give me a pound of those too, please."

"Here's a dandy landing net. Can't bring in trout without a landing net, you know. And that reminds me—breast waders. Why don't you slip into these, just to try them for size?"

I put on the pair he gave me and walked around in them.

"Thermo-ply insulation," Harry pointed out. "Those mountain streams can get pretty icy."

"Say, they do something for me, don't they?" I said, studying myself in a mirror.

"They make you look like a fisherman, that's what they do," said Harry. "By the way, here's a dandy creel—ventilated of course. And a magnetic fly box, so your flies won't blow away on a windy day."

"Great idea, magnetic," I said.

"These round-nose scissors'll come in handy, for slipping off hackle."

"Certainly, we mustn't have hackle all over the place, must we?"

"And this nice skinner does away with messy scaling."

"Excellent."

"Now, in case of a downpour, you'll need this hooded rain jacket."

"Better throw in an umbrella, too. Just in case."

"Remember that fly you told me not to use?"

By this time there was such a mountain of merchandise on the counter, I could hardly see Harry.

"Here's something, if you'll pardon my getting personal," he whispered, holding aloft an object.

"What on earth is that?" I asked.

"A portable toilet."

"By all means. Well, I guess I'll need an elephant to carry all this stuff. Or do you think thirty or forty natives can handle it?"

I made arrangements for delivery, told Harry to throw in whatever else occurred to him, and went to the door.

"One thing bothers me," I said, turning.

"What's that?" asked Harry.

"How did Huck Finn manage with just a string and a bent pin?"

"Beats me," he said.

Were people staring at me on the way to the bus stop? I dismissed the idea.

The bus driver gave me an unusually friendly look as I climbed in. "Trout?" he asked.

I nodded, surprised. Usually they just told me to step to the rear.

"I caught a beauty last Tuesday," he said.

Passengers were beginning to fidget and rattle newspapers, but that didn't bother the driver.

"Let me tell you all about it," he said, getting up from his seat.

"This aisle is the stream and that lady standing over there with the shopping bags is a big boulder," he began.

The lady glared at him.

"Now here I come, approaching from the left, but keeping low," he continued, moving up the aisle in a crouch. "I'm watching out for all the underbrush, see?"

The bus grew very still.

"There goes my fly now, drifting with the current," whispered the driver.

We held our breath.

Suddenly he leaped to his feet, shouting: "Got him! I'm pulling him in now! Into the net—a lunker, four an' a half pounds!"

All the passengers burst into applause and the driver mopped his brow. Then he went back to his seat and resumed driving.

People were still staring at me when I left the bus. I didn't discover the reason until I saw my reflection in a store window, right near where my wife was waiting. I still had on the breast waders!

"Well, it does look like rain," she said.

I ordered rainbow trout when we got inside the restaurant.

"It isn't catfish, is it?" I asked the waiter.

He looked puzzled.

3

It was a beautiful day as I drove upstate towards Paradise Creek. It was the kind of day when convertibles pass you with their noses in the air and closed cars wish they could blow their tops. The sun shone gently through my tinted glass. The road ahead was a white ribbon in an ocean of green.

Paradise Creek! "AN ANGLER'S ADVENTURE OF A LIFETIME," "THE WONDERFUL WORLD OF NATURE AT YOUR DOORSTEP," "A GARDEN SPOT OF PRIMEVAL BEAUTY." That's what the brochure said. And the pictures were so encouraging—a two-year-old boy holding up a trout he had just caught. . . .

I stuck my nose out of the car window and breathed deep.

What a day to be alive! I hoped the trout didn't feel the same way.

My head started reeling with deliciousness and I imagined a minion of the law pulling me over to accuse me of drunken driving.

"Yes," I'd confess. "The air *is* intoxicating."

I pulled my head in before such an interview could materialize and tried to concentrate on the road.

That morning as I prepared to leave, my wife had broken

down when she realized that I actually was going to keep my rendezvous with Nature. Until then she probably thought I was faking, like the time I wrote a letter to the government agency that wanted volunteers for experimental space travel—and nearly mailed it.

"Please be careful," Dora said, handing me my rods, in their shiny new cases.

"The only ones in danger are the fish," I laughed.

"I'd feel better if you were taking along a boy scout," she said.

"A boy scout! What for?"

"To tie the tourniquet, in case you slip on a rock and break one of your legs."

Was there really danger trout fishing? It seemed like such a peaceful sport.

"Dearest, darling, don't worry—if I break a leg I'll make a splint," I said. "A tourniquet is for something else—a sore throat I believe."

In spite of my calm assurances, Dora continued to express fears for my safety as we walked out to the car.

"Watch your ears," she said. "Fishermen are always getting hooks caught in their ears."

"I'll keep my eyes on both of them," I promised.

"And logs. Sometimes they turn out to be alligators."

"Never yet met an alligator that could fool me."

"How about your seasickness pills? Remember what happened last time you went fishing. Should I get them for you?"

"Don't be silly. This is a trout stream I'm going to—not an ocean. How can I get seasick?"

"Fall?"

"*You* can find a way," she said and ran back in the house for the Dramamine.

She clung to me in the street, covering me with kisses.

"Is he off to the war?" a passing neighbor inquired.

"No, to the peace," I answered.

I got into the car and turned on the ignition.

"Oh, dearest, here in the city you know what to look out for," Dora cried. "Taxis, trucks, people jumping out of windows. But out there in the wilderness, what will you look out for?"

"Indians," I said, pulling out of the driveway.

And now here I was, the skyscrapers long gone from my rear vision mirror, ahead only the mirage of a cloistered pool with me standing in it, rod in hand, waiting—gently waiting. My arm moved quickly, a flash, and there it was, wiggling on the end of my line—a lovely, translucent thing of beauty. My virgin catch!

A rude honk scattered the picture and the dream, and brought me back to reality. I was in traffic—crawling, stalling, impossible traffic—the worst I had seen since the day the fat lady tried forcing her way down the up-escalator at Macy's.

"Where's everybody going?" I asked a perspiring State Trooper who was trying vainly to keep the cars moving.

"Paradise Creek," he growled.

My heart sank. How typical of my luck, I thought, to be "up the creek"—before I even got to it. Should I turn back, I asked myself? No, only cowards turn back. I'd go straight ahead. What else could I do? There was a double line on my side of the highway.

I struck up an acquaintance with the driver of a Chevy

next to me. His name was Ed. Married. Three children. Showed me their pictures. Oldest one just like him. Ed's oil burner conked out during the winter. Still giving him trouble. Mother-in-law been with them three years now. None of the other children would take her.

I offered Ed one of my sandwiches. He swapped me one of his. He ate my wife's apple pie. I tried his wife's chocolate cake.

I felt real bad when Ed's lane started moving before mine. Another hundred yards and we would have become real friends.

As we drew nearer our destination, there was increased excitement. People started jumping out of cars whenever there was a momentary tie-up, and putting on boots, or getting rods ready. There were a few cat-calls in my direction when I put on my breast waders, probably because they were so sparkling new, but it was all pretty good-natured, and some of the other fishermen even called over to wish me luck.

I could hardly wait to take my first look at Paradise Creek and at the first opportunity pulled away from the others, in spite of considerable waving and shouting for me to get back in line.

Leaving my car, I walked across a few acres of empty beer cans and cracker-jack boxes, until I came to a crowd of people holding fishing rods.

"Where's the water?" I asked.

"What do you think we're standing in?" they muttered.

On the banks a crowd of spectators sat and watched. If I were a trout, I would have gotten stage fright.

An ice cream and hot dog concession was doing land-

"Who, me?"

office business. And so was a two-story comfort station.

Signs everywhere warned: "*NO* ball playing, bicycle riding, littering, putting camp chairs in the water, or loud shouting when a catch is made, under penalty of death or life imprisonment." But this was a crowd that did not easily frighten. Nearly all the rules were being carefully broken.

"Get any bites?" I asked a fisherman.

"Yes," he said, scratching himself. "All over."

"This place is great for trout," said another fisherman. "They never get caught here."

"Feller caught something yesterday," a voice said.

"Sure. A cold."

"Nope, a real catch. They ran up the flag."

The only flagpole was over the comfort station. There was no flag on it today.

"I can't understand it," said one of the men. "They only stocked this stream a month ago."

"Maybe they stocked it with fishermen," I suggested.

Ed came along, ready to commence fishing. "It isn't what you catch that counts when you go fishing," he said. "It's the Brotherhood of Man. That's what a fisherman enjoys more than anything."

A fist fight broke out nearby.

"Can't they belong to the Brotherhood?" I asked.

"The Wets and Drys are at it again," observed Ed.

"I thought we got that Prohibition thing settled long ago," I said.

"Wet fly fishermen and dry fly fishermen," he smiled. "Which are you?"

"That's like asking a man how he votes, isn't it?" I countered, making a mental note to find out the difference as soon as possible.

I went back to my car and found a policeman writing out a ticket.

"What's that for?" I inquired.

"Parking violation," he said. "You'll have to find a meter."

"This is ridiculous," I said. "Whoever heard of parking meters in the forest primeval?"

"For your convenience we now have drive-in tellers at the courthouse," he said, courteously.

"Thank you," I growled, and drove over to the parking area.

I idled up and down the lanes, looking for a vacant spot. However, whenever I saw one, a fisherman would come speeding up and beat me into it. "A fine Brotherhood of Man!" I thought.

A weather report came over the radio:

> Fair, with increasing crowdedness at
> public fishing streams . . . humidity
> relatively higher.

I shut off the ignition and finished my lunch. Then I read all the old maps in the glove compartment, stretched out on the front seat, and fell asleep.

When I woke up it was late afternoon. I knew it was late afternoon because everybody was backing out and leaving. One car backed out right into my left front fender.

"Brotherhood of Man!" I yelled at the driver, and waved him away. After all, I had come here to relax.

I started to park, then decided to forget about it, and drove back to the state road in time for the returning traffic, instead.

The trooper was still perspiring.

"You can keep this," I told him.

"Who wants it?" he snarled.

When I got home about midnight, I didn't even have the key out when my wife opened the door and asked, "Well, what did you get?"

"A parking ticket and a dented fender," I said, slumping into a chair.

She sat down on my lap and began running her hand through my scalp. This used to soothe me when I had hair. Lately it only reminds me how much I'm losing. However, I can't tell Dora because she still enjoys doing it. Instead, I told her all about Paradise Creek.

"What do you expect in a public stream?" she purred. "After all, there are twenty million fishing licenses in this country."

"Subtract one," I said. "I'm quitting. Tomorrow I'm taking all that stuff I bought back to Harry's Fishin' Hole, and tell him what he can do with it."

"You'll do no such thing," she said. "I've already told my friends you've become a fisherman and they're all jealous of me."

"Jealous of you?"

"They think I'll be getting rid of my husband for a while when he goes on safari."

"Safari?"

"Yes, dear—I found a lovely place for you to go fishing."

She walked across the room and brought back an open magazine. There was a small ad on a back page:

LUKE'S LODGE
BEST TROUT FISHING
IN THE WORLD
CLEAN BUNKS
ROARING RAPIDS, ALASKA

"My God, do you want me to go *there?*" I cried in amazement. The way I had heard it, wives tried to discourage their husbands from leaving the hearth.

"Oh, Alaska's not far," Dora chided me.

"This morning you were worried about me going a lousy hundred miles from here. Now it's all right with you if I go to the North Pole. How come? Have we taken in Rock Hudson as a boarder?"

"No, silly. I just decided I'd rather not be one of those wives who stands in the way of her husband's pleasures."

"So you thought of this?"

"You can take all the time you want to get ready, dear. I'm sure we won't hear from him for at least five or six days."

"Hear from who? Whom?"

"Mr. Luke. I already wrote him. Airmail."

I jumped out of my chair. "That was nice of you!" I shouted. "I suppose you checked my insurance policies while you were at it too?"

"Something's come up and I can't go fishing with you fellows."

"As a matter of fact I did, dear. I know you like things to be in order, just in case."

"All right, that settles it!" I roared, charging out of the room.

"Then you'll go?" she called after me.

"I'll think about it!" I yelled, slamming the bathroom door between us.

A week later I was rather surprised when I went to our mailbox and found it brimming over.

"Darling, is this the end of the month?" I called.

"Why, no. It's only the middle," my wife replied.

"That's strange," I said. "Then these aren't bills."

When Dora joined me in the study she saw me holding my head, the mail strewn about.

"Why dear," she said. "You're ashen grey."

"It's prison pallor," I informed her. "I'm practicing."

"Practicing for what?"

"For my incarceration. Did you write to any other states besides Alaska telling them that I was interested in fishing?"

"Yes, I wrote to about twenty-four. I thought they'd feel hurt if I wrote only to Alaska."

"Well, listen to this. It's from the governor of one of them," I said, and read:

> Dear Friend:
>
> We are delighted to learn of your interest in our state and hope that this special fishing package will be helpful to you. This map of the state will show you the way to some of the most beautiful scenery in the world, to points of great historical interest, and to a variety of recreational areas.
>
> Our state is, of course, unexcelled in its oppor-

tunities for the sportsman. Our lakes and rivers offer the best salmon, trout, and bass angling anywhere. There are many opportunities also for enjoyable canoe trips and for nature photography.

The enclosed booklet lists reliable guides and outfitters and describes their camps, territories, and what they have to offer in the way of sport fishing. A summary of the fishing and game laws is also included in this package, along with the highway routes.

On behalf of all the people of our state, welcome.

Yours sincerely,
GOVERNOR

"How nice of him to invite you!" exclaimed my wife, clapping her hands with delight.

"Very nice," I said, clutching a fistful of letters. "But it so happens that twenty-three other governors have also invited me. If I accept one, the others will be furious. And I certainly don't have time to visit all of them."

Dora bit her fingernails. "Oh dear, what can I do?" she asked.

"You can start packing a valise with some of my things. No, wait a minute—don't bother. I understand that they issue their own clothing in state prisons."

She smiled. "You're making mountains out of hellholes, aren't you?"

"I wish I were," I replied, tossing the mail up to the ceiling. "But these are not simply invitations to come and fish. When a governor writes something, it's a mandate. If I don't do as they bid me, I'll be a wanted man in a lot of those states."

"Oh, that's ridiculous." My wife giggled.

"Oh, is it?" I cried, tossing another handful of papers.

"Look at all these lists of guides and fishing camp proprietors who have been led to believe I'm coming to patronize them. Do you think these honest, hardworking people have sent me pictures of their camps and descriptions of their facilities and taken time out from their chores to ask me to join them, just for the heck of it? Do you think these people and their governors are going to take it lying down when I don't show up? Heck no. They're going to get out their bloodhounds and start hunting for me, that's what they're going to do. In fact, I'll bet they've started already."

Sure enough down the street a dog began baying.

"Relax," my wife laughed. "That's only the Morgan dog around the corner. She's in heat."

"What about this, then?" I inquired, dropping an official looking document at her feet.

Dora drew back at sight of the Great Seal on the letterhead. "What is that?"

"It amounts to international complications," I said grimly. "That happens to be from the Government of Canada. Even they are expecting me."

I picked the letter up and read the last paragraph to her. " 'For the fisherman Canada offers opportunities to enjoy some of the finest fresh or salt water angling to be found anywhere. We do hope we will have the opportunity of welcoming you to our friendly country.' How long will she remain friendly if I don't show up?"

My wife looked at me aghast as the dreadful implications began to dawn on her.

"Fretting won't help," I said, standing up. "I'll run down to Washington and explain the whole thing. I'm certain that war can be averted. After all, there have been more serious provocations."

I put on my hat and went out.

I didn't get as far as Washington. I ran into that same bus driver and he began telling me about more trout he had caught.

That night my wife blindfolded me, spun me around a few times, and I stuck a pin in a map.

Alaska won.

4

When it comes to modern planes, I'm sentimental—I remember well the days when a person could catch up on his reading while flying. That bewildered look on your Uncle Fred's face these days when he steps out of a jet is possibly not due to the speed he was doing—he may be wondering how a magazine story ends that he started.

There was a time when you got two speeches with every plane ride—one when you took off and one when you were about to land. Today we travel so fast there simply is no time for all this verbosity. As an example of jet streamlining, our stewardess said, "Welcome aboard," then after a short pause to catch her breath, added, "we hope you had a nice flight." And there we were coming in.

"Smooth, wasn't it?" I grinned at a lady who had been my seat companion, and got a dirty look. After all, we had only sat together over half a continent!

As we entered the terminal building, a few natives stared at us.

"*Saludos, amigos,*" I greeted them warmly.

"They don't speak Spanish in Alaska," a gentleman behind me chuckled.

"A week of Berlitz wasted," I sighed.

The airport was bedlam. Fishermen rushed by, swing-

"Sure, he's a good guide, but I understand his wife told him to go get lost this morning."

ing rod cases and I narrowly escaped getting stabbed several times. I learned that most of these sportsmen were taking further flights to more distant fishing spots where guides would be waiting for them.

However, "Luke's Lodge," where I had a reservation, was just a short distance away. All I had to do was find the limousine scheduled to take me there.

I reclaimed my things at the baggage counter where officials were eyeing one man with suspicion. His luggage did not include any fishing equipment.

I was starting toward an exit gate with two porters—one just to carry all the heavy woolen underwear my wife had packed for me—when a thin chap, obviously a fisherman, caught up with me.

"H'ya," he said, nervously. "This is my first time up here."

"Really?" I smiled. I thought it might increase his apprehension if I told him it was my first time, too.

"I've fished lots of places," he went on. "Minnesota, Wyoming, Colorado — but who ever thought I'd try Alaska?"

"There's nothing to fear," I assured him. "The Mounties are here to protect us. And, bless them, they always get their man."

"Mounties? I thought they were in Canada."

"To me everything above the United States is Canada," I laughed. "But seriously, this place is not nearly as bad as it was when 'a bunch of the boys were whooping it up in the old Malamute saloon,' I understand."

"Oh, it isn't even 'the Lady that's known as Lou' that

worries me," he confided. "It's innerspring mattresses. I don't know if this place I'm going to has them. I can do without pop-up toasters and my electric shaver but I can't sleep on anything but an innerspring mattress."

"Personally, I'm not worried about any such thing," I said, coldly. "To me a fishing trip means roughing it."

I declined his invitation to join him in the airport lounge for a fast one, and watched him go bolting in alone. The poor fellow had my sympathy.

Outside, traffic was moving along briskly and a queue of taxi drivers looked at me hungrily as I stepped through the door. Nobody was trudging along on snowshoes—possibly because there was no snow—and I was surprised not to see at least one prospector with a mule pack.

A young woman came out behind me and for a moment I thought I heard something—the authentic sound of the North, like a growl or whine from the throat of a distant wolf or coyote. But it was only one of the cab drivers who had spied the young woman, too, giving out with his own variation of the "Call of the Wild."

I found my limousine and while waiting for it to fill up, chatted with the chauffeur.

"Pretty warm, isn't it?" I remarked, affably.

"It's a popular misconception that Alaska is a land of perpetual ice and snow," he said, in a monotone, "and therefore as a result, many travelers are surprised to find the summer months here comparatively warm. Even as far north as Nome, you'll find flowers in bloom. The Japanese current, curving up from the South Pacific, is responsible for this mild climate, with daytime temperatures ranging from fifty-five to seventy degrees. It also accounts for the heavy precipitation along the coast where the weather is similar to Seattle."

The other passengers climbed in, among them the thin chap.

"How's the innersprings?" I asked.

"I've got my fingers crossed," he laughed.

"That's the old spirit," I complimented him.

"Pretty warm, isn't it?" a man in front remarked.

"It's a popular misconception that Alaska is a land of perpetual ice and snow," the chauffeur began again, "and therefore as a result many travelers are surprised—"

"Don't bother," I cut in. "I'll tell them."

Now commenced a twenty-mile scenic ride across the face of this last great frontier. We were all too enthralled with the exciting panorama unfolding outside our windows to speak. (Women usually say, "Isn't this lovely?" or, "I wish we had a picture of that!" Men just drink in the sights and say nothing.) It was hardly necessary, therefore, for the chauffeur to break in on our thoughts as he did.

"I'll shoot the first bastard who says, 'There's gold in them thar hills,'" he suddenly threatened, as some ice-capped mountains came into view.

"How about grizzlies?" one of us asked after a while. "Seen any lately?"

"Only last week," the driver answered. "We visited an aunt of mine in New York, and I took the kids over to the Bronx Zoo. They sure are big."

"Who, the kids?" we asked.

"No, the Alaskan grizzlies. They're the biggest animal in

North and South America, you know," he said, proudly.

"Good for you," we congratulated him.

The terrain got rougher and rougher. We saw nothing but glacier formations, trackless tundra, and spectacular wilderness.

Panic suddenly gripped me. Why had I come here? What was I trying to prove—that I could survive? And if so, at what terrible cost?

While I was groping for the answers, our car turned off the road and went up a rocky hill. Buzzards looked down at us ominously from their perch atop a proscenium arch inscribed LUKE'S LODGE. I closed my eyes and steeled myself for what lay ahead.

When I opened my eyes I sat blinking in amazement as the others got out of the car. There were a half dozen neat fieldstone buildings, manicured lawns and a turquoise swimming pool. Guests were frolicking in the water, sunning themselves on chaise longues, or playing croquet.

"What the hell is this—Grossinger's?" I muttered.

A florid-faced man in a gayly colored plaid shirt hurried over and started pumping hands with everybody. I finally got out of the car and he pumped hands with me, too.

"Welcome, gents," he said. "I'm Luke, your genial host. I'll show you to your cottages."

"Cottages?" I echoed, and dug in my pocket for the ad my wife had cut out of the magazine. "This mentions only clean bunks."

"My land, you must have gotten that out of an old issue," Luke laughed. "That's the trouble with dentists' offices . . ."

"You call this Alaska?" I grumbled.

"Alaska, *U.S.A.*," Luke reminded me. "We're just trying to keep up."

A couple of girls in bikinis passed by.

"What kind of bait do we use for those?" chuckled one of the fishermen.

"Looks to me like they got *you* caught," roared another fisherman.

"Listen, Mr. Luke," I protested. "I don't want a place with luxurious accommodations that caters to families. Nor do I want one that features such things as snack bars, Broadway entertainment, and colored television. All I ask is a little retreat where the comforts of home are completely inaccessible. I want to be a real fisherman, like the kind my wife has read about."

"See here, young feller," said a portly man with white hair who had come up alongside me, "I've been fishing trout forty-seven years and I'm sick and tired of roughing it. I say if this here is a place where we can fish and have comfort, I'm staying. There's no law says a fisherman's got to suffer."

"Hear! Hear!" said the others.

"How about innerspring mattresses?" asked the thin chap.

"We got 'em. Beauty Rests," said Luke. "And next year we're gonna have a championship golf course behind that there gulch. Got feelers out now for Middlecoff or Palmer as pro."

"Hot diggety," said a fisherman.

A tennis ball hit me on the head.

"Eight clay courts," added Luke. "Hope you brought your rackets."

Chimes sounded from one of the buildings. "You're just in time for cocktails, gents," said Luke. "Dinner's in an hour."

"Black tie?" I inquired, sarcastically.

They all started after him, while a team of Eskimo bell-hops gathered up the luggage.

"How about me?" I shouted. "What am I supposed to do—become an outlaw?"

"You can try Pop Jeeter's place," said Luke, pointing to a distant mountain.

I followed his finger. "What's that? Mt. McKinley? How am I supposed to get up there?"

"I'll drop you off later—by 'copter. But I'm warning you—I can't be responsible for what you'll find."

"Thanks," I said.

"Now, c'mon and have a drink meanwhile," invited Luke.

He didn't have to ask me again. The girls in bikinis were coming back and this time they looked determined. I figured I might as well make the best of things.

5

"Here we are," said Luke, above the noise of the 'copter. "You can get out now."

"Wouldn't it be better if I waited for you to land?" I asked. We were still about ten feet off the ground.

A shot rang out.

"Jump!" ordered Luke.

I jumped and he tossed my baggage out after me. Then he waved, and went whirling away over a distant gorge.

There was another shot, right near me this time. I dove headlong behind a rock and lay very still, tasting the Alaskan dust.

"All right, Sonny," someone said. "On your feet an' stick 'em up."

"What, my feet?" I asked, looking up at a grizzled old coot, holding a gun.

"No, yer hands."

I did as he directed.

"I never took a shot at wildlife before, only animals," he said. "Otherwise, I wouldn'a missed."

"You needn't apologize," I said.

"Now that I gotcha, what am I gonna do with you?" he asked still keeping the gun on me.

"Do you happen to be Pop Jeeter?"

"I be."

"Then all you have to do is teach me how to fish trout. That's why I came here."

"You ain't one of them Howard Johnson rest'rant people?"

"No, Mr. Jeeter. Though I have eaten in many branches of that great chain."

"I'll be durned. I thought sure you wuz part of the invasion."

"What invasion?"

"From the states, Sonny. Nothin' but motel people, real estate people, rest'rant people an' what not comin' around here ever since we joined th' Union. Durned if I know whether it wuz a good idea."

He lowered his gun. I did likewise with my hands.

"Haven't you gotten anything out of being affiliated with the U.S.A., Mr. Jeeter?"

"Sure—three extra letters on my address. Everything's changin' up here—'specially the fishin' camps. Looka that neighbor o' mine y'just come from—he's offerin' continental breakfasts, valet service, square dancin', and lavender bed-sheets! A fine howdy-doo when fishermen start livin' like that!"

"Not I," I said. "I came up here to rough it."

His eyes opened wide. "Then you've come t' the right place, Sonny! There's no rougher place than this one. Stay here an' I'll make a real trout fisherman outa ya."

"That's all I ask, Mr. Jeeter."

"Call me Pop. What's your name, Sonny?"

I told him. I even spelled it out. But I could have saved

my breath. Jeeter kept right on calling me Sonny.

"Follow me an' I'll show you to y'r quarters, Sonny," he said.

I picked up my things and followed him through the brush.

"You'll learn real quick, provided y' ain't stupid."

I was silent.

"Y'ain't, are ya?" he asked.

"Ain't what?"

"Stupid."

I didn't answer.

He stopped walking and peered into my face. "Well, I guess it ain't your fault," he said when the examination was concluded.

"I happen to have a Ph.D.," I said hotly.

"It don't matter," he shrugged. "I'll do my best with ya, anyway."

We came to a clearing and I saw something that looked like a tool shed.

"This is th' guest house," Pop Jeeter said. "My place is over there."

He pointed to another shed with the word PRIVATE painted crudely on the door.

Neither place looked like it was A.A.A. recommended.

"Step in an' make yourself at home, Sonny," Pop said, throwing open the door of the "guest house."

I did.

The furniture was early Robinson Crusoe. A table, a chair, two bunks, a cracked mirror.

Obviously, the chambermaid had not been in yet.

"Who's in the other bunk?" I asked.

"Mister Albemarle. Sad case. Been here six months an' ain't caught a trout yet. Stays in the stream all th' time."

I had heard that there were some strange cases among fishermen.

Jeeter watched me unpack my fishing equipment.

"What's this?" he asked, picking up something.

"That's a catcher's mitt," I said. "Can you figure out why the tackle store man sold me such a thing?"

"Nope. An' I can't figure out why he sold ya these either," said Pop, pointing to a pair of frog feet and a badminton set.

He took my rods out of their cases and examined them carefully.

"When'd you buy these?" he asked.

"Last week," I said. "Why?"

"They're ob-ser-leet," he said. "Happens all th' time. No sooner do ya buy fishin' equipment than they turn around an' improve on it."

He picked up a rod. "Too heavy," he said.

He picked up another rod and found that one too light.

He picked up something else and pronounced it perfect. It was a broomstick that had been standing in the corner.

"If there's anything I need, can't I run down to the store for it?" I asked.

"Sure," he said. "If y' can run twelve days. That's how fur it is."

I shuddered. Never had I been more than a few blocks from the nearest delicatessen. Suddenly I envied those who sprang from sturdier stock.

"Roughing it, my foot! I happen to live in a place just like this!"

Pop examined the flies I had brought. "These should all be in somber shades," he said thoughtfully. "We can use the Silver Doctor, Coachman and mosquito. Can't use any o' the wet flies 'cept the bucktails, optics and bivisibles. Ah, good—ya brung some nymphs, I see. Of course, later on ya can make all these y'rself. I do."

"You do what?"

"Tie my own flies. All y' have t' be is a little handy."

"You mean you actually construct your own flies?"

"Sure. Nothin' to it. Lotsa fishermen do."

I felt ashamed. When I was a kid I had torn wings off flies. Perhaps here was my chance to make restitution.

"First thing y' have t' remember is that fish can't tell color," he said. "And they can't smell."

"Ah, but fish do smell—terrible," I said.

He overlooked the hideous joke. "So all y' have to do is make something that *resembles* a insec'."

I stared at him dumbly.

"Here," he said, taking something out of his pocket. "What does this look like?"

"Lint?" I asked.

"It's a mayfly," he said, and pulled out something else. "What's this?"

"Old cigar butt?"

"Winged ant."

He tried me once again.

"Wad of gum?" I ventured.

"Stone fly," he corrected me.

"Do you mean to say that trout actually mistake these

objects you're showing me for authentic members of the insect world?"

"Hook, line 'n sinker, Sonny."

Were trout cockeyed, I wondered?

"Of course insects ain't easy to imitate," said Jeeter.

"I can do imitations—Como, Elvis, Cagney," I said, "but insects I never tried."

"It takes years o' experience," he said. "And now if you'll 'xcuse me, I'll fetch you a nice cup o' coffee."

While Pop was gone I fooled around with a fly-tying kit the tackle shop had sold me. But after a few minutes I gave the whole thing up as a silly kindergarten game. "Only God can make a tree, or insect," I decided.

However, when Pop Jeeter came back with my cup of coffee, he looked at the pile of junk I had left on the table, and whistled. "How'd those dern pests get in here?" he asked, and started slamming the table with a frying pan. "I'll get a flitgun in here first thing t'morrow," he promised.

I finished unpacking and followed him outside. Purple shadows were lengthening over the bleak, ghostlike canyons.

"Well, how d'ya like it here?" Jeeter asked.

"I'm going to recommend it to some of my friends," I said. I meant the ones that were fugitives, of course.

We sat down on some logs.

"What's your parent river?" Pop asked.

I looked at him, uncomprehending.

"Where'd ya fish when you wuz a boy? All fishermen had a creek, or pond. . . ."

"I never had any," I said. "There was a canal near us, but it was so polluted, only fish that were looking for typhoid would swim in it. We once had guppies, but we didn't have them long. They're cannibals. I always wondered who ate the last one."

Pop waved his arm in the direction of a rushing stream just yards away and said: "Right here we got trout, artic char, steelhead, pike, salmon . . ."

"I think it's a wonder that so many different fish can live together in the same place, at peace with one another," I said.

"Peace nothin'!" he expostulated. "They're always tryin' t' eat each other up, too!"

"The little monsters!" I gasped.

"Th' little beauties, y'mean," Pop said, his face lighting up. "Take rainbows, f'rinstance. Know anything about 'em?"

"Only that Judy Garland used to sing a beautiful song about one. Also, that there's a pot o' gold at the end of them."

"I mean rainbow trout. This stream is so full of 'em, they hafta make reservations six months in advance t'get in—just like a fancy resort."

"Sounds like the fish wouldn't be particular how heavy the tackle or what kind of flies was waved at them."

"That's where you're wrong, Sonny. Fish are smart—durn smart. Sometimes I think they're almost human."

Was that sound in the stream a fish taking exception to the remark?

"You just try wavin' flies at trout any old way and yuh'll never catch 'em."

"Why is that?"

" 'Cause trout know fly castin's a sport an' they want to make it interestin'."

I chewed on that remark a while.

"Of course, you're lucky, Sonny, bein' dropped on th' doorstep of one o' the few who can really teach this bus'ness."

"I'll always be grateful for what you show me, Pop."

"I ain't sayin' y' couldn't learn in one o' them other fishin' camps but at least here you won't be distracted by a lot o' girls walkin' around with tennis rackets."

"I have never seen a tennis racket that could distract me," I said.

Pop got up and yawned. "Well, goodnight, Sonny, we'll start t'morrer," he said, and went into his shack.

I watched the orange ball drop over the horizon where a Russian outfielder might have been waiting to snare it with his gloved hand. Then I sat there, bathed in dusk and thought: real fishermen have the right idea. Take Pop Jeeter. It's getting late, so what does he do? No staying late at the office for him, no crowded supper clubs, no theatre parties . . . he just goes to sleep.

The other way was complex, crazy . . .

This way was sane, logical . . .

I could be this way, I thought. Rugged, a man of the outdoors . . .

But what about my wife? She was—well, so civilized . . .

Perhaps we could work something out. She live in her world, I live in mine . . . and yet be together . . .

Suddenly I came out of my reverie. The shadows were gone and I and the night were one and the same. I looked but I couldn't see—not even my hand in front of my face. I listened, and all I could hear was the sound of a thousand beasts eating—or being eaten.

Which way was my shack? I sat very still, staring into the black, trying to get it figured out.

Why hadn't Pop Jeeter left one little light burning? At home there were always ten electric lights burning. If I didn't go around turning them off, there'd be twenty. Right now my wife probably had that many turned on.

Which way should I go? The wind came out of the night and hurried my decision. I rose and started to move along, inch by inch, arms outstretched—like a sleepwalker. Then I felt myself falling, falling, into an endless abyss. Well, two feet anyway. I was in the stream!

I staggered out, soaked, and started moving again. Was there a stump or rock to fall over? If so, I found it.

I hadn't called for help heretofore because I was afraid Pop Jeeter might lose respect for me. Now I didn't care. "Mr. Jeeter! Help! Help! Help!" I called.

I might as well have called for the union cavalry. There was no sound of reinforcements coming. Only the sound of wind, and the creatures of the night.

I sat down and recalled that long ago when I was a child, I had been lost, too, and had wound up in a police station with the sergeant's cap on my head and a lollypop in my mouth.

Now there was no lollypop, no sergeant's cap and worst of all, no police station.

A minute before my teeth had been chattering. Now, all of a sudden I felt warm and cozy . . . warm and cozy. Then I remembered something and jumped to my feet, panic-stricken. Hadn't I read somewhere, perhaps in Jack London, that death by freezing was always preceded by an illusion of warmth? Warmth and coziness?

I started running again. Running and stumbling . . . madly, blindly . . .

At last I went down, down, down into empty nothingness . . . into oblivion . . . into Nirvana . . .

I awoke to the smell of frying bacon, and broad daylight. Pop Jeeter was sitting a yard away, eating from a tin plate and eyeing me admiringly.

"Ah, you're up, Sonny!" he said. "Why didn't you come inside last night instead o' sleepin' here on th' ground right outside th' guest house? Lord, I thought you wuz only foolin' when y' said y' wanted t' rough it. But I guess y' really meant it. Only nex' time, Sonny, at least cover yourself up with a blanket."

I tried not to let Pop see my hand shake and my teeth chatter as I took the cup of hot coffee he handed me, and gulped it down.

"You're gonna make a fine fisherman, Sonny!" he said. "A mighty fine fisherman, jus' wait and see. Now, eat up an' we'll start th' lessons!"

6

"READY t'meet Mother Nature?" Pop asked.

"Ready," I said, apprehensively.

I'm always apprehensive when I meet a lady for the first time.

He led me into my baptismal water.

"There's lots o' ways t' catch trout," Pop said. "Dry fly, wet fly, worms, spinners, nymphs . . . I happen t' like dry fly 'specially when th' water's clear. Y'gotta have clear water fer dry fly."

"So you can see the trout?" I asked.

"C'rrect," Pop said, stopping suddenly and looking up to the heavens.

"Is something missing?" I asked.

"Yep, rain. Any fisherman'll tell you it's always gotta either look like rain or be raining when he goes fishin'. One fisherman I knew claimed it always rained on his day off, no matter what day he picked. Happened t' him fer twenty years. He now works for drought areas. They invite him out fishin,' an' they get rain."

The cold water lapped at my thighs and I was grateful for the waders.

"Notice anything, Sonny?" Pop asked.

"Yes, the water's getting deeper."

"Imagine! My wife wanted me to stay home today!"

"Heck, no, it's all shallow here," he said. "I know every foot of this stream."

No sooner did Pop utter the words than he sank into the water over his head. He came up coughing.

"Guess that's a foot I fergot," he spluttered, and started forward again, with me at his heels.

At last he seemed to find a spot he liked.

"You go over there, 'bout ten feet away," he said.

"I can't," I answered.

"Why not?"

"You're standing on my foot."

Finally we were all set.

"Most fishermen believe in castin' upstream so they can retrieve their line as the fly comes down," Pop said. "But there's no hard an' fast rules in fishin'."

I sighed with relief. "I'm glad," I said. "I have enough rules to follow at home: 'Use Rear Door for Deliveries,' 'No Smoking,' 'All Books Must Be Brought to the Library for Renewal,' 'Keep to the Right,' 'One Way Street.' Who knows? Perhaps I only took up this sport as a form of rebellion."

"Hold on, Sonny! We got rules out here too," Pop said. "F'rinstance, when y' see Mister Trout swimming along, what do y'suppose he's lookin' fer?"

"Miss Trout?"

"No! He's surface feedin', that's what he's doin'. Lookin' for insects. That's where dry fly fishin' becomes an art, Sonny. Y' gotta make your fly behave like it's a real one so Mister Trout'll take it!"

I knew what my wife would say. She'd say it was a dirty

trick, misleading a poor little fish into thinking you were giving him something to eat when all you were really giving him was the business.

"Now, another rule is y' gotta study everything around ya," Pop went on. "Th' color o' th' water, th' sky, th' reflection o' the trees, th' wind . . ."

"I always do so I can tell people what kind of weather I had on my vacation," I laughed.

"No, that ain't the reason. It's t' help y' decide which fly t' use," Pop said.

He looked in his fly box and I heard him muttering about Grizzly Kings, March Grounds, and Rube Woods.

"Heck," he finally said, picking one, "I always come back to this good old Coachman."

I waited to see what would happen next.

"See that leaf floatin' out there?" he asked.

I nodded.

He brought his rod up overhead very quickly in a short motion, paused for a split second until his line straightened out behind him, then jerked the rod forward to the original position.

The fly went sailing out and landed in the water a yard from the leaf!

"It took me forty-five years t' learn t' do that," Pop said, proudly.

I tripped on a stone and grabbed my rod to keep from dropping it.

There was a choking sound from Pop.

I looked around. My fly had shot out and landed on the leaf!

"It was an accident," I said. "I was falling and . . ."

George Washington's father just patted his son on the head. At that moment I would have been grateful if Pop Jeeter did the same thing and just let me grow up to become the father of my country.

Instead he staggered over to a rock and leaned against it. "Who'd y'ever see cast like that?"

"Whitey Ford," I said.

"Who?"

"He's a baseball pitcher. Famous for picking runners off first base."

Pop yawned.

"I'll just stretch out here, Sonny, and tell ya what t' do," he said, climbing up on the rock and lying down.

I waited until he made himself nice and comfy.

"Bring your rod tip up," he said. "Not too fast . . . keep that elbow at your side . . . bring it ahead again . . . that's better . . . pay off more line . . . don't hold it back as it runs through th' guides . . . turn it a bit before it lands with your rod tipped . . . keep your rod up . . . watch those elbows . . . don't take out more line . . . cast an' pause . . . let that fly down . . . now retrieve slow . . . try short, quick lifts . . . now try a slower retrieve . . . sweep it with your left hand . . . don't forget to keep touchin' your automatic every once in a while . . . y' don't want a lot o' loose line . . ."

A freckle-faced barefoot boy in blue jeans came along while Pop was talking, dropped a piece of string with a bent pin in the water, and caught a foot-long fish.

". . . don't pause too much," Pop went on, unmindful of anyone else's presence. "Just long enough fer th' line t' straighten . . . not too short now or th' fly'll snap off . . . don't let it hit th' water with such a splash . . . y'll frighten 'em away . . . aim a little ahead o' the spot where y' want it t' fall . . . check your line now . . .let your fly float down on th' water . . . the leader an' line'll follow . . . bring it ahead again . . . don't tense up . . . relax . . . stop usin' your whole arm . . . keep all th' action between th' wrist an' elbow . . ."

"What's he talking about?" asked the boy.

". . . check your forward cast," Pop continued, "keep th' fly travelin' through the air so it dries . . . you got enough line out . . . don't let out any more . . . let that fly down easy . . ."

The boy shrugged and walked off with his fish.

Pop's voice faded away. I went over and looked at him. He was fast asleep.

I wandered downstream. Would I ever get to learn the mysteries of a stream, to fathom its depths, to really *know* it?

How unfortunate, I was thinking, that my wife could not see what a fine picture of virility I made, sloshing along with my rod in hand and the Alaskan pastoral for a background, when along came a glass-bottom sight-seeing boat, filled with rubberneckers.

"There's a quaint old character with a fly rod," I heard a lady say. "Get his picture, Joe."

"I'm not a quaint old character!" I yelled. "Just because I didn't shave this morning . . ."

"Anybody with a fly rod is a quaint old character!" she retorted. "Now, please hold still!"

I held still.

"He certainly is getting to know these waters."

There was a click, and the boat passed on, almost engulfing me in its wake.

As I dried myself, there was a cheerless "hello" from the bank.

It was a fisherman. He looked glum.

I walked over. "No luck?" I asked.

"Yes, plenty," he said, holding up a string of fish. "But that's the trouble. My wife won't let me bring them home."

I hadn't considered what Dora might say if I came home with a fish. What did most wives say?

"It's a decision a fisherman sometimes has to make," he said. "Either his wife—or the fish he's caught."

He thought a while.

"I guess I'll take Helen—I've known her longer."

I took his string of fish and went back to the rock where I had left Pop.

The old man was still talking in his sleep. "Let that fly down easy now . . . watch that slack . . . stop using your whole arm . . ."

It was late afternoon when Pop awoke. He looked at my string of fish and said: "You're pickin' it up fast, Sonny. Just keep listen' t' what I say."

It hurt me to tell him how I had gotten the fish, but I did.

"Well, anyway you hold 'em like an old timer," he said.

"How do you want it—broiled or mounted?"

7

"How DID I become a fisherman?" Pop asked, after dinner, as though I had brought up the question. He put a match to his pipe, sucked on it several times, and began: "We lived miles from any river an' I never even saw a fish 'til I wuz about fourteen. Ma an' Pa were vegetarians—they wouldn't eat anything that could swim, fly or crawl. One day this feller comes past my house an' he's carryin' a long pole. I asked him what's the pole fer and he says it's fer eatin'. I never heard o' a pole bein' for eatin' so I foller this feller and asked when he's goin' t' begin eatin'. He says just as soon as he gets near a river. So I keep follerin' him fer four days until he comes to a river. It was the first river I ever seen an' he puts that pole into the water with a string an' hook on it an' blamed if pretty soon there ain't somethin' wigglin' on the end. I thought this was a trick o' some sort because whenever it rained around our house my ma would say we had a reg'lar river outside, but I never seen nothin' wigglin' in our river. Anyway, this feller pulls the wigglin' thing out an' I says 'What's that?' an' he says 'Ain't your ma and pa never taught you nothin'? This here is a fish.' I told him my ma and pa don't eat nothin' that swims, crawls or flies an' he says maybe it's because they ain't never tasted perch. So in a few minutes he cooked that perch an' after we ate I went right home an' started packin'. 'Where you goin'?' my folks asked and I says, 'I'm goin' t' seek my fortune an' when I say river, I mean a place that has things in it that wiggles.' So out I went an' I started driftin' from spring t' brook, an' from river t' creek meetin' all kinds—bankers, railroad tycoons, business exec'tives. But I never held it against 'em fer what they were, cause when they went fishin' they dressed like bigger bums than me."

The pipe had gone out, and Pop fumbled for another match. It gave me a second to reflect. One of the insidious things whispered about the very rich was that some of them had their own privately stocked streams. It should only happen to me!

"I learned a little about fishin' from ever'body," Pop went on, "but the most I learned was from a barefoot boy. Ask any fisherman, he'll tell ya a barefoot boy knows more about fishin' than anybody. This one knew more than any other barefoot boy. An' he shoulda. He was lots older. He was about fifty-two. Got arrested one day fer not wearin' shoes. He wuz on Main Street at the time. Got six months. They called it indecent exposure. Anyway, by that time I c'd tell without even lookin' at a stream where the rills feedin' it were, in what deep pools th' trout might be lurkin', an' whether a rainbow was hiding behin' a rock or in front of it. I started takin' on any little pond that other fishermen would laugh at. 'If there's anything alive in there, Jeeter'll catch it,' they said, an' they were right. I was gettin' t' think like a fish—fish sense they call it, Sonny, an' it started t' scare some folks. It even scared me some-

"Now that Ernest has his own private stream, he misses other people's 'No Trespassing' signs."

times. I used t' wake up nights thinkin' I was chasin' a fly! Then this terrible thing happened t' me."

He relit his pipe and waited for the sound of my voice, to prove that I had been paying attention.

"What happened, Pop?" I asked.

"I wuz in trouble. Couldn't catch nothin'. I wuz like a feller who had never fished before. Worse. Those fellers have beginners' luck. Ain't no such thing as old timer's luck. I kept tryin' for weeks. One body o' water after another. I started losin' so much weight worryin', I could hardly lift up a rod."

He seemed to be trying to erase some terrible memory.

"Even Babe Ruth used to have slumps," I said.

He nodded.

"Well, Sonny, I came out o' my slump all right, but I wuz gonna live t' wish I hadn't. Late one day I was castin' my streamer, an' retrievin' it over and over again with no luck when I saw this trout movin' into the shoals. He wuz th' biggest brown I had ever seen, makin' a mighty ripple in th' water as he swung around. 'Mister Brown,' I said t' myself, 'you're gonna help ol' Pop make his comeback.' I cast towards him an'—I had him! My line started runnin' out, an' I let it go for a couple of seconds, countin' up to about five, but slow—then I checked it. Wham! I could feel this feller's weight, an' I think he weighed as much as me. Now I had my work cut out fer me, Sonny. I had t' try t' keep my boy out o' the rocks 'n roots 'n snags. I started puttin' on th' pressure t' keep him in th' open water. He started comin' in t' me, an' I stripped in as fast as I could

"Business is great—that's my trout fishing chart."

with th' sweat pourin' from me like I had th' fever. I started feedin' him line, at the same time bein' careful not t' have a tangle o'slack, otherwise it might trip me up or get fouled on some o' those snags. Now he wuz goin' away again—it got dark n' I couldn't see him too far, but I could feel 'im, runnin' outa the water and over the trees. This wuz a fish that didn't jus' know how to swim, Sonny—he could run an' fly, too! But I didn't care what he did. 'Mister Brown,' I yelled, "tain't no use. Man is th' Supreme Bein' on this earth, an' you're just a fish no matter how you run or fly—so you might as well give up.' Well, he's out there somewhere in the water laughin' at me—I could hear him—and then suddenly he starts comin' in t'me—nice and slow, like he's tired an' ain't got no strength left at all. How wuz I t' know Mister Brown's a great actor as well as everythin' else? All I'm thinkin' is here's one trout that's gonna wind up stuffed on my wall so I can sit back an' look at him all through th' cold winter t'come. While I'm thinkin' he starts with a flash again, shootin' in between my legs, in and out, in and out, so fast I got dizzy." Pop swallowed.

I could hardly wait to hear the conclusion. How was this epic struggle going to end?

"Before I knew what that trout's up to, I'm all tied up in knots, an' spinnin' aroun' like a top. 'Mister Brown, let go,' I pleaded. 'Let's you an' me call this a draw.' But he jus' kept me spinnin' aroun' 'til my line ran out, an' then—plop—I fell in the water. It took eight 'r nine other fishermen t' untangle me an' by that time I was th' laughingstock o' th' stream. Word about it spread. So I went inland an' retired. Then one day it started rainin' fer forty days an'

"Then he pulled, and I pulled, and finally I got away!"

forty nights an' there wuz a flood. So I went up on the roof an' started fishin' again an' pretty soon I wuz back t' normal."

He knocked the ashes out of his pipe and went into his shack.

It was still an hour before dark but I wasn't taking chances on getting lost again.

I went into my shack, too.

8

I AWOKE before dawn. From Pop's shack came the rhythmic sound of snoring. I listened to it a while, trying to fit it to the tune of Cole Porter's "Begin the Beguine." Then I had an idea. I'd get in a little casting practice before Pop awoke and surprise him with my improvement.

I unhinged my rod, put on my bathrobe and slippers, and stepped outside. A squirrel, or its Alaskan counterpart, stared at me for a moment as though wondering if I were a nut worth cracking, then scampered away.

Carefully, I took the position Pop had prescribed—with my back to his cabin—pretending I was in the water.

"Start with line extended in front, about a couple of rods length . . ." I said aloud, as though it were Pop directing me.

The squirrel returned and took another calculating look at me.

". . . now hold rod at ten o'clock, raise quickly to twelve o'clock, and check," I continued, self-consciously, "aiming for the sky overhead."

Did I hear that squirrel snicker?

My line was caught on Pop's roof in back of me!

I gave a little pull. Then I gave a bigger pull. One thing must be said for nylon. You can pull a piece of roof off with it. I know, because that's what happened to a piece of Pop's roof. However, Pop went right on snoring without missing a beat.

I changed my position. I faced Pop's shack.

The squirrel changed his position. He faced me.

This time I had no trouble with my backcast.

It was my forward cast.

Again the squirrel snickered.

Again it cost Pop a piece of his roof.

I beat my way through the brush about a hundred yards, to a spot where a cluster of trees lifted their leafy arms not to pray, I suspected, but to catch my line. To my amazement, I unfurled one perfect shot, straight into the strike zone.

There was a whinnying sound in the brush and by the dawn's early light, I caught a glimpse of something that looked like a pair of giant antlers, and a frightened animal fleeing for its life.

When I got back to camp, Pop was making breakfast. I didn't mention anything about a reindeer or caribou getting away, or ask if he'd ever heard of one being caught with a dry fly.

Instead, after changing my bathrobe and slippers for conventional fishing garb, I announced that I would demonstrate my improved casting technique.

I whipped the first one out and there was a clink as something landed in the bushes.

"Very nice," said Pop. "We didn't need that coffee percolator, anyway."

I tried again and we lost our bacon.

"Too much fried food ain't good fer ya," he philosophized.

"Sure, only God can make a tree, but why did He have to make one right there?"

I found out why Pop was so undisturbed a few minutes later. He had already eaten.

After dining on hardtack—or hard tacks—I joined Pop in the stream.

"Trout fishing takes patience," he said. "Th' feller who gives up right away because he ain't caught anything, will never make a good fisherman."

"I've got patience," I said. "I don't care if it takes me a half hour."

"Look at Albemarle over yon," said Pop, pointing to his other guest downstream a way. "Six months an' he still ain't caught nothin'."

The man had a beard two feet long.

"C'mon out," Pop pleaded with him. "At least long enough to shave."

"Not until I catch one," answered Albemarle, firmly.

"Didja ever see such stick-to-it-ive-ness?" Pop whispered in awe. "He won't move."

"Maybe it's *stuck*-to-it-ive-ness," I said. "Maybe he *can't* move."

Pop tossed Albemarle a sandwich and we left him there, staring at the stream.

"Now, today we'll deal with th' wind," said Pop. "What does the word 'wind' bring t' mind, Sonny?"

"A pleasant picture on the avenue," I replied. "Skirts blowing, necks turning . . ."

"On a trout stream, wind means only trouble," said Pop. "That is, unless y' know what t'do."

He cast his line out and as he did so, on cue, the wind started blowing.

"Blast it," said Pop, trying desperately to control the line which was twisting around him. "When a thing like this happens, Sonny, there's only one thing a wise fisherman can do. He turns around and casts with th' wind."

Pop turned the other way. The wind, however, turned right around with him.

"Nature *will* have her little cap-ree-ces," he said, all tangled up in his line.

Dust and tumbleweed were flying and trees looked like they would be uprooted any second.

Pop took refuge under a rock. I joined him. "What are we doing now?" I asked.

"We're conservin' th' trout supply," he said.

He took a deck of cards out of his pocket. "This is one o' my favorite rocks."

"You once caught a record trout here?" I asked.

"Nope. I once won three hundred dollars in gin here. D'ya play?" he asked, shuffling the cards.

I stared. He riffled with a dexterity I had never seen except in movies about gamblers on Mississippi River steamboats.

"Er, look," I said. "The wind's died down."

We stepped out from behind the rock.

"One thing about wind, Sonny—it blows lots o' insects over th' water an' th' trout come up fer feedin'," Pop said.

"One more thing about wind," I said, "it blows hats off. Excuse me while I try to find mine."

I went downstream looking for it.

Albemarle was jumping up and down, shouting ecstatically, "Hooray! At long last I got something . . ."

It was my hat.

Finding anything but a fish on one's line can indeed be one of life's darkest moments.

I expressed my sympathy to Albemarle and went back to Pop.

"That was wrong o' Albemarle," he said, "lettin' out a great big holler. There may be other fishermen about an' a lot o' noise'd scare away their catch."

His fly landed on the water. I could see a swirl.

"YIP-PEE!" Pop screamed.

A kingfisher two miles away took wing in a hurry.

"Now, Sonny, watch closely," Pop said, breathing hard. "Improper handlin' c'n lose that fish now. Notice I'm holdin' th' rod straight up and lettin' this feller knock hisself out. There he goes! He's tryin' t' make a run fer it! Let him try! See how I'm keepin' that line good and tense, Sonny! Oops, watch that rock—gotta keep him away from that! What's that? I know I'm holdin' th' rod horizontal now. That's so I c'n keep him away from that rock! No, I'm not tired, Sonny! Why should you ask such a crazy question? I been catchin' 'em like this since before you wuz born! No, he's not pullin' me, I'm lettin' him take me down t' th' shallow water. Oops! There he goes again! I gotta keep him above me! I'm tirin' him out now! No, I don't need no help. I'm gettin' my net ready. Now I scoop. See how careful I'm doin' it! This baby can still break loose! There, I'm gettin' him in head first! Now he's in deeper! Takes years t' learn this, Sonny! Oh, gosh—Oh, no! He got away! He got away . . ."

Pop sat down on a rock and started to sob. . . .

"You are lucky! The tread is still good on that one!"

I remembered something my wife had packed for me and ran back to the shack for it.

"Here, Pop," I said when I returned, "take this. You'll feel better."

He took one. "What is it?"

"Tranquilizer. In the city everybody takes them," I said.

In a few minutes color came back to Pop's face. "Well, Sonny, we might as well call it a day."

A voice suddenly spoke up from the bank. "It's ridiculous to leave now, gentlemen."

We turned and beheld a youngster, impeccably dressed for fishing, with fly rod in hand.

"Are you related to that barefoot boy who was fishing here yesterday with a bent pin and a string?" I asked.

"That's my brother. He has a James Whitcomb Riley complex," the youngster said.

He took a pencil and pad out of his pocket and made some notes.

"What's that you're writin'?" asked Pop.

"Just some mathematical equations, sir," the boy replied. "According to my calculations, a hatch of gigantic proportions is about to develop in this stream."

"Children nowadays have very scientific minds," I whispered to Pop.

"Who don't know about hatches?" Pop muttered.

"My theory is this, gentlemen," the boy continued. "Eggs dropped by female flies on or in these waters, have gone through the larva and pupa stage. As is well known to all entomological students, the next step is the imago, or fully developed insect."

"Why don't he tell us somethin' new?" growled Pop.

"As you are doubtless aware," the boy went on, "female flies develop their eggs on or in the water of a stream, and the egg then sinks to the bottom where it hatches into the larva."

"Fresh kid," grumbled Pop.

"During the pupa stage it sometimes attaches itself to a stone or log at the bottom of the stream, and after a period of one to three years the insect, or nymph, is about ready to rise to the surface and take wing. This metamorphosis, of course, is one of nature's great phenomena."

"Keep it clean!" warned Pop.

"It is my contention that we are minutes away from a hatch such as I have just described. Moreover, preliminary tests lead me to suspect that this hatch will be *hymenoptera* —insects which have a wasp waist. So, gentlemen, select your flies accordingly."

We dug into our fly boxes as the boy lifted his wristwatch and began the countdown: "10 - 9 - 8 - 7 - 6 - 5 - 4 - 3 - 2 - 1 . . ."

Hundreds of insects rose to the surface and simultaneously, the noses of hungry trout appeared above the surface of the stream.

"I've got one!" I shouted, after a few minutes.

Pop and the boy were too busy netting trout themselves to offer me congratulations.

Downstream, I noticed, Albemarle was still staring into the stream, catching nothing.

After an hour or two, the boy walked Pop and me partway back to camp. "I wish I could spend more time with you, gentlemen," he said, "but I must go home and continue work on my thesis 'The Effect of Barometric Pressure on Successful Trout Fishing.' "

"Smart kid," I said to Pop, when we were alone.

"I thought he was a little too clever for his own good," grumbled Pop.

But I noticed that he looked after the boy admiringly.

9

NEXT day on our way to the stream I noticed a few rows of headstones set neatly in the ground.

"What's that? A graveyard?" I asked, jokingly.

"Yes," Pop said. He seemed reluctant to talk about it. I pressed him.

"It's the final resting place of some so-called fishermen we had up here," he stated finally.

"Why did they die?" I asked.

" 'Cause they broke what we call th' 'Code o' Ethics.' Got themselves killed."

"Accidentally?"

He shook his head.

"Murdered?" I gasped. "By whom?"

"Other fishermen," Pop said.

"I thought fishermen were very gentle people."

"As a rule. But they can be driven mad. Take that feller there. He borrowed flies an' never returned them. Th' one next t' him there had a habit o' bargin' in just when somebody had a nice quiet piece o' stream staked out fer himself."

"How about this one?"

"He'd keep throwin' a flashin' spinner from th' opposite side o' stream, right smack where you wuz droppin' a fly.

Very disconcertin'. Even a judge'd agree stranglin' wuz too good for him."

"What did that next fellow do?"

"Nothin'. Not a blamed thing. Never did an ounce o' work in camp. Jus' sat aroun' an' played a harmonica. Played lousy, too."

We walked down another row. "These are th' ones who jus' couldn't leave their troubles home," said Pop. "Talked politics all th' time . . . stock market . . ."

"Poor fellows," I said, and bared my head.

"They deserved t' die," said Pop firmly, without taking his hat off.

We entered the stream.

"A fisherman must have good manners," said Pop. "He must act refined at all times, never be rude or inconsiderate o' others—he must be a perfect gentleman . . ."

His voice trailing off warned me, but too late. Before I could get out of the way, he came charging forward, swinging his net, and knocked me over.

I lay there in the water watching him flail about like a madman.

"Durn it," he groaned, stopping at last. "A grayling, an' I almost had him!"

He helped me to my feet and wiped my face with a rag he used for putting filament on his flies. "Where wuz I?" he asked.

"You were knocking me over," I said.

"I mean b'fore that."

"You were saying how a fisherman should behave like a perfect gentleman at all times," I reminded him, pointedly.

"Yeah," said Pop. "Will y' remember that?"

I promised.

We walked along upstream.

"A good pair o' ears is also important," said Pop. "If a fly fisherman had ears like a dog or deer, you'd see 'em pick up at ev'ry li'l sound—th' plop a fish makes when he rises, th' suckin' sound he makes when he takes in a insect . . ."

There was a loud crashing sound nearby, followed by a low, ominous growl.

My blood froze.

"Did you hear that?" I asked.

"Hear what?" asked Pop.

A large brown creature peeked out of the bushes a yard in back of him. Then came two more of the same specie.

I yanked Pop away in a hurry without explaining.

"What's the idea?" he demanded.

"Did you ever hear the story of Goldilocks and the three bears?" I asked.

He nodded.

"Well, I didn't just see Goldilocks," I said.

We pushed through the water a few hundred yards and perhaps Pop imagined I was laboring.

"Havin' trouble?" he grinned.

"Why?"

"After all, Sonny, yer not used t' all this exercise. Not that I blame ya. This here is a swift current. Ever walked agin' a current before?"

"Only once," I said, "and got a ticket for jay-walking."

"There's a right way an' a wrong way o' wadin'," said Pop. "Right way is like this—pushin' one foot nice an' slow

"Don't be silly! They're always dangerous."

ahead o' th' other, an' pausin' 'til y' have a nice, firm grip."

I waited for him.

"Now, y'bring th' other leg fo'ward," he said.

I snapped some pictures.

"Now y'got both feet t'gether, right?"

"Right," I said.

"If y'wanna sit down 'n' rest, go ahead, Sonny."

"I'm not tired," I said.

"Go ahead, sit down," Pop insisted.

"Why?"

"Because I'm tired." He gasped and flopped down on a rock. "Hurryin' is a mistake some fishermen make. When ya take yer time y'can study stream conditions, sky color, scenery . . ."

Pop took his deck of cards out and shuffled them. "Feel like playing now?" he asked.

"Please, let's fish," I implored him.

He put the cards away, picked up his fly rod, and became the teacher again.

"Fishermen hafta be careful t' avoid accidents," he said, whipping the rod.

On the back cast, the barb of the fly got caught in his left ear.

"Ow!" he yelled.

"My wife warned me about that," I said.

"Did she tell you anything else?" Pop asked.

"Such as what?"

"Such as how t' get this thing outta my ear!"

"Do you think I dare try such an operation?" I asked.

"I can't get Albemarle t' do it!"

"But I don't have a license to practice medicine in this state."

"I don't care!"

"Come to think of it, I don't have a license to practice in *any* state."

"Okay," said Pop. "Don't help me. Just let me walk aroun' with this hook hangin' in my ear fer the rest o' my life."

I asked what I could do.

"Can you stand the sight of blood?" he asked.

"Other people's yes, not mine."

"There's two ways o' doin' this—one way you c'n cut it out with a knife."

I picked up a knife.

"Wait a minute! I ain't permittin' nobody t' whittle off one o' my ears," he shouted.

"What's the other way?" I asked.

"Pull it out."

"That will hurt."

"I c'n take it."

"I can't. Not your ear."

"Listen, Sonny, I'm the captain o' this camp and what I say goes. Now I say 'pull'!"

I pulled.

Dear Diary, I would pen that evening. *Today I caught a two-ounce left ear.*

Pop carried on for about twenty minutes.

Finally, I said, examining him, "At least you won't be like Van Gogh. Your ear is still there. Shall we fish now?"

" 'T ain't no use. There's no rise," he said.

"I'm getting a rise out of all this," I answered, not knowing what he was talking about.

"I mean the trout. See how smooth the water is? They ain't risin'."

"Let's throw in some yeast. Maybe that will make them rise," I said disgustedly.

We sat on the bank and waited. I did some writing on the back of an old envelope.

"Watcha writin'?" asked Pop.

"I'm figuring out what sitting here is costing me. And let me tell you, it adds up to a small fortune just to wait for some fish to stick his head out of water."

I hated myself for sounding like a mercenary. Did other fishermen's minds work this way?

" 'Tain't my fault," said Pop. "Maybe y'should o' gone to a weddin' instead."

"A wedding?'

"Yep. *Rise* and old shoes!" He roared, slapping me on the shoulders.

I groaned. Corny jokes, yet!

"Do you know what they call me in the city?" I asked. "They call me 'The Dynamo.' "

"You just gotta sit tight, Sonny," said Pop.

"Why are people always sitting tight? Why don't they ever sit loose?"

"I dunno, Sonny."

There was a ripple out on the stream.

"It's a rise," I whispered.

"I don't see nothin'," said Pop. He had taken his cards out again.

"When I'm at the office I think about the fishing; when I'm fishing I think about the office."

There were more ripples.

"It isn't raining," I insisted.

"Wanna play now?" Pop asked, splitting the deck.

"All right, you've been asking for it!" I snapped.

We played.

He took me for eighty dollars.

"Are you *positive* you never worked on a Mississippi River steamboat?" I groaned, watching those expert fingers of his dealing.

Then my luck started to change. I won back five dollars, then four, then six. I had a streak going . . .

"Durned if I don't think you were right, Sonny," Pop said, looking at the water. "There *is* a rise."

He grabbed his rod and rushed into the stream—with my money.

I followed him.

"You're what we call an ideal fishin' companion," said Pop.

"What does that mean?"

"We are temper'ment'ly suited t' each other. I like your company."

"You mean you like my money," I said.

Just then a nose came out of the water. Hurriedly, I cast. My fly landed about two feet above where I aimed—and the fish took it!

A few minutes later I had a fair size trout in my net.

"Too bad," said Pop.

"What do you mean 'too bad'?" I asked.

"Any fisherman'll tell ya," he said, "worst thing that c'n

happen is t' catch a fish on your first cast. Means y' won't get another all day. A man's always better off not catchin' nothin' th' first fifty times he casts. But I hope catchin' this feller makes you feel better after our game."

"If you think an eight-inch trout is going to make me forget sixty-five dollars," I retorted, "you're sadly mistaken. Now kindly release this wretched creature. He reminds me of a very dear friend."

"Lots o' fishermen hardly ever keep anything they catch," said Pop. "They just fish fer the sport."

He slid his hand down the leader and got a firm grip on the hook.

"Won't that hurt him?" I asked.

"Naw—fish have diff'rent nervous systems from us."

He pulled out the hook.

"Ouch," I said.

The fish didn't say a word. He just lay there in the water without moving.

Pop pulled him back and forth very gently until his gills started working. When he let go, the trout swam off, as good as new.

"On behalf of his family, thanks," I said.

For the remainder of the day we caught nothing.

"Maybe they've gone on a hunger strike," I said, discouraged.

"They're eatin' th' natural flies," Pop said.

It was true. The trout were coming to the surface and eating all around us.

"Perhaps ours are not Duncan Hines approved," I said.

"We gotta study th' hatch," said Pop.

"Unfortunately, we got hungry on the way back with this one."

"Don't bother looking in the water," I said. "They're all on me."

We tried several kinds of flies, with no success.

In desperation I got out my fly-tying kit and made a scale model of an insect crawling on the back of Pop's neck.

"Who's gonna take that—a whale?" asked Pop.

I trimmed it down to size.

Just before we quit, a despondent trout came along, looked at the fly, and figured that it was as good a way to go as any.

"He musta been frightened t' death by this thing," said Pop, examining the fly disdainfully.

Two hours later I was alone in my shack when there was a knock on the door.

It was Pop. "Er—how'd y' tie that fly?" he asked sheepishly.

I told him I couldn't reveal the secret. "My lips are sealed . . . like the Stradivarius people . . . these things are kept in the family . . ."

10

I OVERSLEPT, and when I got down to the stream Pop was already in it, fishing. He stood absolutely motionless. A small bird came to rest for a second on the end of his pipe but Pop didn't even blink an eyelash.

"Good morning," I said.

He jumped. "Never make noise like that, Sonny! You'll frighten th' foragin' fish!"

I apologized.

"A fisherman has t' learn t'be absolutely quiet anywheres near a stream," he cautioned me, as I cast out into the water.

Something started tickling my nose.

"I'll never f'get," he said, "I had a feller up here once who kept sneezin' all th' time . . ."

I held my finger under my nose.

". . . 'course he'd always pick a time when th' trout wuz foragin'."

The tickling was getting worse.

"An' natchurly whenever this feller sneezed I'd always have t' say 'God bless you.' "

I bent over and submerged my head in the water, where only a trout could hear my little spasm.

"If there's anything a man deserves who has th' gall t'

sneeze when trout are foragin', it's not to have anybody say 'God bless you,' " Pop concluded.

A minute later, just as a trout opened his mouth to take my fly, I heard a very loud "AH-CHOO!"

"Damn it!" I exclaimed.

"What's that?" asked Pop.

"I said 'God bless you,' " I lied.

"Mebbe I'm comin' down with somethin'," Pop said, and left the stream.

I didn't hear from him until about an hour later, when he called: "Any luck?"

This is a standard greeting among fishermen. If fish could pick up lingo like parrots, they would probably learn to say "Any luck?" first. Although, it would be silly for one fish to ask another such a question. If a fish hasn't been caught, he's obviously having all the luck he needs.

Pop came over and found me reclining on a rock, calling: "Come out, come out, wherever you are . . ."

"What's that supposed t' be?" he growled.

"It's a game I played when I was a child," I explained. "Didn't you ever play it?"

"I never had time t' play games," he grumbled. "All I ever did wuz fish."

"There's a trout under this rock and I'm trying to coax him into coming out," I said.

"Playin' games won't do it," argued Pop. "Y' just have t' wait. Sometimes th' fish are shy."

"I've never been too forward myself," I answered.

"Just be patient. He'll come t' you," said Pop, and left me alone.

I waited an hour.

Perhaps Pop was wrong, I thought. Perhaps that trout would never come to me. Perhaps he was waiting for me to come to him. I decided to take the first step.

"May I introduce myself? My name is Izaak Hoff," I ventured.

The trout's nose poked above the surface.

"How do you do?" said a voice.

Was I going mad? Had that trout really spoken to me?

Then I saw a reflection in the water and it wasn't a trout at all. It was Mr. Albemarle, Pop's other guest. He was holding a small fish.

"Did you just catch that?" I asked, turning.

"Yes," he said soberly. "My first trout after six months and five days . . ."

His lips were quivering.

"Go ahead and cry, if it will make you feel better," I said.

Albemarle threw himself on the ground and shook convulsively.

"I'm all right now," he said, sitting up after a while.

Pop came over. "Why, there's tears in your eyes," he remarked.

"Yes, but they're tears of happiness," Albemarle told him, showing his catch.

"What're your plans now?" asked Pop.

"No more fishing, that's for sure," said Albemarle.

"Maybe you'll start catching them all the time," I said, "now that you've broken the ice."

"I'm not taking chances," Albemarle shrugged. "I'm quitting while I'm ahead."

"What will you do?" I asked.

"Maybe go back to golf. *Qui vivra verra,*" he said, stroking his beard. "Meanwhile, if you'll excuse me, I'll go shave this thing off and clean up my lines."

"Speaking of lines," I said, "I think I'll drop my wife one."

"Ain't no letterbox aroun' here, Sonny," laughed Pop.

"I don't need one," I said, getting paper and pencil.

I wrote:

Beloved:
There isn't a woman around here as beautiful as you. I miss you terribly.
Me
P.S. There isn't a woman!

I rolled up the note, put it in a bottle and threw it into the stream.

"Expect her t'get that?" asked Pop.

"All our neighbors get their mail in bottles," I said. "Only one thing bothers me—she hates notes in pencil."

"Only one thing bothers *me*—that wuz a deposit bottle," said Pop. "I coulda gotten a nickel fer it at th' tradin' post."

For several days afterward we had success fishing. We caught quite a few trout which Pop identified as rainbow, brown, or speckled. It was like playing tag, though, because we let most of them go.

Then one day the trout didn't want to play any more. It was depressing.

Pop tried every trick he knew. He looked in all the rills and deep pools. He even led me upstream to a section he had never tried before.

"Any luck?"

"This stream is all fished out!" he shouted, finally.

An osprey dropped a half-consumed fish on his head.

"Don't contradick me. This stream is all fished out!" Pop shouted again.

"Why are you yelling?" I asked.

"In case any other fishermen are listenin'. We don't want a crowd aroun' here."

"Suppose it's true?"

"We'll go to a more remote stream," Pop said, cheerfully. "Fishermen are always doin' that."

"Why?"

"It's tradition'l. Th' remoter th' stream, th' better th' fisherman."

"I didn't think there was anything more remote than this place," I muttered.

"Of course, sometimes 'fished out streams' really ain't fished out at all," Pop said. "It's jus' that fishermen who tried 'em were prob'ly doin' something wrong. Mebbe they were lettin' their leaders an' line float over the fish too far in advance o' th' fly. Mebbe they weren't fishin' th' rise. Mebbe a million an' one things. Once I fished one o' them 'fished out streams' an' I caught me a couple o' eighteen inch rainbow an' a big brown in ten minutes. 'Fore I had 'em in my net, word got aroun' an' all these fishermen who had given up that stream were back. By that time I wuz on my way t' another 'fished out stream.' "

He chuckled reminiscently.

"How about this stream?" I asked.

"You can take my word, Sonny," he whispered, looking

around carefully for the osprey, "this one is *really* fished out. C'mon, we'll get in th' boat an' try it past th' rapids."

As we left the stream, I glanced back. Did I see a rise, and did I hear one trout say to another: "Okay, they're gone now—we can stop playing dead"?

I helped Pop load supplies into a rubber boat with a specially built frame and cawlings to keep us dry.

"Where d'ya wanna sit?" he asked. "Front or back?"

"Front," I said.

It didn't really matter what seat I chose, I soon discovered, because when we hit the rapids a few minutes later, the boat started spinning around like a top, and half the time Pop was in front and I was in back.

I did what any frightened landlubber would have done under the circumstances—I buried myself under the cawlings. I have never cared for boats, anyway, except the ones I used to play with in my bathtub.

"Jus' keep steerin' an' we'll be all right," I heard Pop say.

I peeked out. He was under the cawlings too!

"Man overboard!" I shouted.

"Who?" he shouted back.

"Me. I'm leaving," I said.

But before I could make good my threat, our boat bounced off a rock, or tree trunk, and went flying through the air.

When I came to I saw that we had landed on a small stony beach. One of my inlays was loose.

"Well, here we are," Pop was saying, as if he had known all along where we were going.

"I can't stand him either, but he's handy with motors."

We set up the tent and made camp in a few minutes. My wife would have fussed around, moved a few rocks here and there, maybe hung curtains . . .

In a little while Pop and I were trying out the new stream.

"Look," Pop said, "th' water here is so clear we can spot 'em in th' deepest parts."

It was true. We could see trout beneath the surface, nibbling away.

We offered the trout our flies. They went right on ignoring us.

An hour passed without any luck.

"Try a cricket," said Pop.

I did, but the trout didn't take it.

"Try a beetle," said Pop.

The trout didn't take that, either.

A small brown finally took something I offered him.

"What was that?" asked Pop, after I brought him in.

"A piece of my hatband," I said, putting away my hackle scissors.

I wanted to release my fish but Pop was not in a benevolent mood.

"Ever been to a post mortem?" he asked.

"Whose?"

"A trout's. We gotta find out what they're feedin' on."

After the operation was over we found out, but our luck did not change.

"Maybe they've got union waiters down there," I said.

"Remember what I taught ya," yawned Pop, turning away. "Patience, stick-to-it-ive-ness . . . never give up . . ."

"Where are you going?" I asked.

"T'sleep," he said, and went into the tent.

Perhaps the solitude did it to me. Perhaps solitude has done it to other fishermen. I started talking to the trout.

"My uncle talks to fish," I could hear a little niece of mine say, who has always acted suspicious of her uncle's sanity anyway.

"Here, boy," I said, when a trout came up close.

Or, when one looked feminine, "Here, girl."

I even tried out my three lessons in hypnotism on them and for a while thought I had a trout completely in my power. He stopped swimming and stood absolutely motionless in the water.

"Your eyelids are getting heavy," I said.

That's when my act fell apart. He didn't have any eyelids and left me with two lessons to go.

That evening, just as I was about to creep into the tent to join Pop in slumber, I decided to make my bed outside instead.

I inflated my nylon air mattress, covered myself with blankets, and got settled.

Sleeping under the stars is a strange sensation when you're not used to it—especially when you believe that there is life on those other planets. And I happen to be one of these believers for a very obvious reason. Who else could turn on the lights up there night after night but living creatures?

So when you are a believer as I am, you lie there looking up at those lights and before you know it you begin feeling self-conscious as though the people living in the apartment above you suddenly pulled back the ceiling and are watching you in bed.

Thus I lay, trying to forget those billions of eyes staring down at me, when I heard footsteps.

I looked around and saw two little men with antennae on their heads, and fly rods in their hands, heading down toward the river bank. Pop was snoring away in the tent and I was loathe to disturb him, so I got up and followed the two creatures myself.

"Hello," I said.

"Take us to your leader," one of them bade me.

"He's sleeping," I replied, nodding in the direction of the tent.

"I mean take your leader to us," he said. "Don't you know what a leader is? It's something to tie on the end of this line."

I started to get one for him.

"How's the fishing here?" asked the other little man.

"Out of this world," I said.

"How would *you* know?" they snapped.

I got the feeling that they didn't want me around and went back to my nylon air mattress.

"Some strange kinda animals wuz around here last night," said Pop next morning, examining footprints on the bank.

I didn't say a word.

I let him go on thinking they were animals.

11

I WAS busy retrieving my fly next afternoon when I turned and found Pop with his hand cupped to his ear as though listening to the sound of distant music.

"Do you hear it, Sonny?" he asked.

I listened carefully.

"Well, do ya?" he asked again.

I shook my head.

"Concentrate," he said.

I was anxious to get on with my fishing. "I hear," I lied. "What is it?"

"It's countless rushin' rivers, tumblin' streams, an' quiet lakes," he said, trembling.

"Good," I said, to humor him.

"Well, we'll hafta be goin'," said Pop, gathering up his things.

I looked at him in amazement. "Where?"

"To them countless rushin' rivers, tumblin' streams an' quiet lakes," he said, surprised.

I studied his weather-beaten face. He was perfectly serious.

"All anglers go when they hear The Call," he said.

"But we just got here," I protested. "The fishing is good. It just doesn't make sense to leave."

"Th' man who can resist that call just ain't an angler," Pop challenged.

"Dammit," I muttered under my breath, and started packing.

"You're gonna make a fine fisherman someday, Sonny. Jus' you wait an' see." Pop grinned, picking up a twig and scratching on the ground with it. "This map'll give ya a rough idea where we're goin'."

"Don't tell me where," I said, wearily. "Just tell me how far."

He looked into space and I could feel the wheels in his brain gyrating like an IBM machine.

"Six days," he said, finally.

My leap into the air would have made a Columbia River salmon green with envy. "Now you listen to me, Rand McNally," I bellowed. "I don't care what that map of yours says—I'm not going to budge one inch more than three days from here."

Pop's face fell. "I ain't never heard o' rushin' rivers, tumblin' streams an' quiet lakes bein' that close," he said, miserably.

I couldn't stand seeing him with that hurt look. "How about four days?" I pleaded. "I was gassed in World War I."

He refused to bargain.

"All right. Make it six days," I said helplessly. There was a clear picture in my mind of what his fate might turn out to be.

Pop's face lit up.

"You're a card, Sonny," he said. A card . . ."

"And this is the guide who didn't find one spot where they were biting!"

The word reminded him of the deck in his pocket and he started to reach for it.

"Show me that map," I said, quickly.

He began using the twig again. "This here is the spring where we are, an' it's fed by this creek over here which is fed by this snow-capped mountain down over there."

I leaned over his shoulder to watch. Maybe with luck we'd remain in this hemisphere.

"Now over here," he went on, "in-noomer-able lakes an' rivers thread th' land an' there's thousands o' bays an' inlets t' which comes all th' game fish. In fact, there's great sport fishin' an' lake trout or graylin' can be taken with flies in nearly all these clear springs. That's just a day from here."

"Then why can't we fish there instead of going so far?" I asked.

"Because them waters are too popular with visitin' fishermen," Pop said. "Only last year I seen three people with fly rods."

"That settles it," I said. "We can't fish where it's so congested."

Would I get to hate people the way Pop did? If I had my choice on a desert island, which would I choose—Marilyn Monroe or a fishing rod?

"Main species here," Pop went on, making a mark with the twig, "are spring cohoe, kokanee salmon, steelhead, kamlooks, coastal cutthroat, brown and char-lake trout, an' arctic graylin'."

It sounded like the census people were on their toes up here.

Pop made another mark on the ground. "This lake over here is supposed t' be the original habitat fer ouananiche, or landlocked salmon," he said. "But there's a little dispute over it."

"What kind of dispute?"

"Th' chambers of commerce o' forty-two other lakes claim th' same thing."

I stood up and stretched.

"Over here I once got me a 145-pounder," Pop said, scratching another spot reverently.

"Trout?" I asked, incredulously.

"Nope. Woman."

The disbelief on my face made him blush.

"She wuz fishin' an' our hooks tangled. I told her she wuz th' best lookin' rainbow I ever seen."

"What did she say?"

"She said that wuz th' trouble with fishermen. A girl can't trust 'em because they got such lines."

Pop chuckled. "She sure hadda great sensa humor."

Romance in Pop Jeeter's life! I hadn't conceived of such a thing.

He sighed. "Dolly an' me spent all season fishin' together. Then one day when I woke up, she was gone. Sometimes I wonder if I jus' dreamed up th' whole thing."

"Did you ever find out what happened to Dolly?"

"I always figgered she jus' went upstream t' spawn."

He forced himself back to his map. "This bay over here is a good area fer trout, although there ain't no caterers at present fer anglers."

"I was really after trout."

"Did you ever go looking for her?"

"Nope. Ever'body tol' me there wuz plenty o' other fish in th' sea."

"Were they right?"

"Sure, I found plenty o' other fish, all right. But no Dolly. No other woman either. Now these lakes over here have been sys-tem-attic-ly stocked with rainbows origin'lly planted in that river up there."

"Do you ever miss her?"

"Sure. We got long, cold winters up here."

"What would you do if you ever ran into Dolly again?"

Pop lit his pipe. "I'd have her stuffed an' mounted, so I could at least look at her once in a while. Pollock an' mackeral are caught in coastal waters but you ain't interested in them."

"Right now I'm only interested in Dolly."

"This area's got brook trout, arctic graylin', char, lake trout, walleyed pike, rainbow trout an' smallmouth bass."

"Nothing else?"

"Er—yes."

"I knew you were holding out, you old son-of-a-gun."

"There's Rocky Mountain whitefish," he said, and turned to finish his packing.

I watched him for a minute, then folded the tent.

"We'll hafta cut through th' timber land t' get t'this place," said Pop.

"Start cutting," I said.

The long trek began.

We hadn't gone very far when I noticed that from time

to time Pop would take a coin out of his pocket, flip it up in the air, and catch it.

"Why are you doing that?" I asked.

"T'help me decide which way t'go," he said. "Heads I go one way—tails th' other. All guides do that once in a while."

I took a piece of bread out of my knapsack and started dropping crumbs as we went along.

"Watcha doin' that fer?" asked Pop, looking back at me.

"Little Hansel did it to keep him and his sister Gretel from getting lost when their wicked step-father took them into the woods," I said.

"I ain't yer sister Gretel," he growled. "An' furthermore I know where I'm goin'."

"I know, too," I said.

Pop looked surprised. "Y'do?"

"Yes. You're going around in circles."

"R'diculous!" he snorted.

"Then why am I getting dizzy?"

Pop pointed down at two separate pairs of footprints in the earth. "If we're goin' aroun' in circles, Sonny, how come we ain't caught up with these two fellers yet?"

"Because those fellows are us," I said, wearily.

Pop tried fitting his shoes into the footprints.

"You should try that at Grauman's Chinese Theatre in Hollywood some day," I said. "Janet Gaynor had the tiniest pair you ever saw."

"Jus' gimme a chance t' read th' signs," said Pop, sniffing the air.

NOT RESPONSIBLE FOR PERSONS LEFT HERE
FROM JANUARY 1st TO DECEMBER 31st.
STATE OF ALASKA

"While you're at it, read this one," I said, pointing to some crude lettering on a tree:

Pop sank down on the ground and started moaning. "I guess I'm gettin' old, Sonny. We're lost."

I had to get him on his feet. The winter snows were only three months away.

"We can't be lost," I hollered. "You're a guide, and everybody knows a guide never gets lost. He's like a St. Bernard dog. Did you ever heard of a St. Bernard dog getting lost?"

There was a sound in the bushes and a St. Bernard dog came walking out, looking around uncertainly.

"I'm sorry," I said to the St. Bernard. "We don't know where we are either."

The dog sighed and kept going.

Why hadn't I picked an Indian Guide? They were supposed to be infallible.

"Well, there's only one way to get out of here," I said. "Which way do you think is the right direction, Pop?"

He pointed a finger.

"That settles it then," I said. "We'll go the other way."

The trek continued, over rocky ledges and slippery slopes. Every few minutes I kept asking Pop how he felt.

"Fine," he said. "Fine and dandy. Just peachy."

"Then would you mind getting down off my back and walking?" I asked.

"Eeny, meeny, miney, mo . . ."

We came upon a surveyor busy making linear measurements, and waving to another surveyor some distance away.

"Thank God," I cried. "Maybe they can tell us where we are."

"You're right on the Alaska Freeway," said one of the surveyors. "When this road is finished it'll take only two shakes to get from downtown Los Angeles to Juneau."

"What'll ya take t' make it four shakes?" asked Pop, bitterly.

"Why, man, the whole outdoor fraternity can hardly wait for this Freeway to be finished," said the other surveyor. "They say that every station wagon in North America is just itching to try it out."

"My forwardin' address is Siberia!" shouted Pop, rushing back into the forest.

I caught up with him and we continued the death march. Stiffness and soreness beset every bone in my body but every time I slowed up, Pop's hand stole into the pocket where he kept his deck of cards, and I plunged on doggedly.

"At this rate it'll take us less'n six days t' get there," Pop complained.

I stopped walking. "Do I infer that you were counting on this trip taking six days so you could toy with me at gin?" I yelled.

Pop hung his head. "I jus' thought it would be easier walkin' for ya if ya didn't hafta carry all that money."

"Thanks," I said bitterly. "If you really want to be helpful, you can carry the toothpicks. After all, I'm carrying the boat, the mattresses, the tents, the food, the clothing, the cooking utensils and the fishing rods."

"Sure, Sonny," Pop said amiably. Then he looked around and feigned surprise. "Oops—how d'ya like that? There's the stream now!"

I was so bent over from the load on my back that I hadn't noticed.

"You shoulda tol' me you wuz tired before this," grinned Pop.

"I was only panting because I was thinking of Gina Lollobrigida," I said, trying to straighten up.

"C'n I help?" asked Pop.

"Only if you have the phone number of a chiropractor," I said.

If my temper was about to explode, the scene that now lay before us acted on me like a tranquilizer. All I could do was stand there gaping at the forest beauty and filling my lungs with its fragrance. Alpine-sized wild flowers grew in profusion everywhere, and there were countless yellow cedars, balsam firs, and tideland spruces spreading over the rounded hills and rimming the stream. Also, I could see thickets of alders and willows, as well as aspens and large cottonwoods stretching out as far as the eye could see.

"Beats salt water fishin', don't it?" chuckled Pop.

"How do you mean?" I asked.

"Mebbe them ocean fishermen got a bigger variety o' fishes, but when do they ever get t' see pictures like this?"

I had to admit that Pop was right. From what I had seen so far, there was no doubt that sweetwater fishing did offer extra dividends in scenery.

"Why I've known anglers who spent more time admirin'

th' water hyacinths than they did fishin'," said Pop. "In fact, once a rhymin' feller came up t' my place with $1200 worth o' fishin' equipment an' all he took home was a poem. Wish I remembered how it went."

"I remember how one went that a fellow next to me wrote when I went deep sea fishing," I said. "It went like this:

" 'Captain, captain, have you seen?
This guy's face is awful green.' "

"Nature sure has been 'ceptionally kind t' these parts," said Pop, peeling a banana and throwing the skin into the stream.

He climbed up a little hill for an exploratory look around while I got ready to try out this newest spot.

Was I the first human to go wading into the crystal waters? The stillness gave me no answer.

What hidden mysteries did the brook contain? Ignorance caused my imagination to run wild. One of those mental pictures flashed before me and I could hear two trout talking . . .

"There's a thousand other lakes jus' like this one," called Pop.

"Let's spend a year in each," I said, joyously.

"F'm up here they look like scattered di'monds."

I sighed. "My wife only likes the kind she can wear."

What was I missing here? Was it the friendly brochure that seemed to go with every lake and stream—the welcoming note sounded by skillful writers and hungry Chambers of Commerce?

"All I ask is a quiet stream somewhere . . . *any*where."

I closed my eyes and visualized a propaganda pitch for the stream I was standing in:

> A vacation in Lake Jeeter (look who I was naming the place after!) is a treat your entire family will long remember and treasure in its memory. Let mom and dad, Uncle John and Aunt Sara, and the twins Molly and Cholly experience the cool shade of the rock and driftwood, the unforgettable blue waters and the green forest. Let them run helter-skelter through nature's own quiet garden while cares and worries disappear and perspectives are restored by that master weaver of dreams—the Majestic North. Relax and have fun at Lake Jeeter. Breathe deep of the pure, pine-scented, filtered air. Fish among your choice of a thousand blue lakes. Bathe in safe waters and enjoy beaches that provide fun and safety. Or in winter, skate, ski, or ice-fish.
>
> Let your work-worn nerves unwind, tensions disappear and your appetite be rejuvenated as you play and sleep at Lake Jeeter, while the beautiful sound of the carillon chimes from the tower in nearby Jeeter Town sounds the knell of parting day.
>
> Yes, a friendly welcome awaits you and yours at beautiful Lake Jeeter, where there are ample motel accommodations for one and all. So plan your visit now, and enjoy, if only briefly, our rich natural heritage . . .

First impressions are important, and I resolved that my first cast in Lake Jeeter must be a good one. I took care to have enough space behind me and let go, remembering that in fly casting it is the line which is cast and not the fly.

There was a light splash exactly where I had mentally marked a target.

"Bullseye!" Pop exclaimed, pausing in the act of putting up the tent.

How did he know where I had aimed? Was he clairvoyant, and if so wasn't there a law against people like that going around with a deck of cards?

"I aimed there, too," Pop chuckled, answering my unspoken question.

"No more gin with you," I said, and moved over to a spot behind a rock where sharp-eyed trout couldn't see me. My next casts were upstream and I waited patiently for the fly to drift back to me with the current.

"I'll fix th' pan," Pop called, starting a fire.

It was the signal of my graduation from appenticeship, and acceptance into the elder tribe. Pop was depending on me to bring home the trout. I swelled with responsibility and pride.

An hour later I was still retrieving an empty line and cold fear gripped me. Had Pop's act been premature? Was I not ready yet? Would I let him down? And the pan?

At last there was a strike! My reel sounded the joyful note of success at last and I let the fish run for a few seconds before I pulled gently, and felt his hungry ferocity.

I played him carefully from pillar to post, watching all the snags. Sweat bathed me and I realized I was tenser in battle than ever before. Was it because this was for dinner?

Relax, I said to myself. In photographs anglers never seemed to look worried about anything except when they'd be able to get away fishing again.

I finally brought my trout in, using the net before he got too near the tip of my rod.

We needed one more, I decided, and cast again. This time there was immediate success—my first one's brother, or sister (Pop hadn't yet explained the fishy facts of life to me), sticking his nose out of the water and catching the fly almost before it landed, like a line drive.

I wanted to make this party really mine so I laid my two little victims out on a rock and, avoiding their eyes, inserted my knife in their belly vents and slit up toward the gills. The entire guts came out in one piece and for a fleeting moment I heard my name over a hospital loud speaker: "Calling Doctor Hoff . . . please go to surgery . . ."

The illusion led to some reflections on the medical profession. Did surgeons trout fish to relax? Would I trust myself in the hands of one who did?

Placing ferns and leaves between my trout to keep them from sticking together in the creel, I strode triumphantly back to camp.

I was Caesar entering an empty city. There was no applause. Pop was fast asleep—or pretending.

All right, you old rascal, I thought—I'll even cook them for you.

I fried my trout in bacon grease until they were golden brown. The smell, I'm sure, would have brought Emily Post on the double, like a starving lumberjack. Pop, however, slept on.

"Wake up," I said, shaking him. "Dinner is served."

His eyes remained closed but a little smile played around his mouth. "Ah, dinner," he murmured. "I c'n see it now—a thick porterhouse steak, smothered in mushrooms an' onions . . ."

Then he started sniffing and looked around. "Dern it,"

"Royal Coachman. Er . . . I mean, suture."

he said, the smile vanishing. "Fish again. Fish yest'day, fish th' day b'fore, fish t'morrer. . . ."

I stood there with my skillet sticking out, listening to him.

"D'ya mind if I go on dreamin', Sonny?" he asked. "That other meal I wuz havin' tasted jus' wunnerful."

His eyes closed again and the little smile re-appeared.

I dined alone.

12

THERE came a day when Pop asked me what was the matter.

I didn't answer.

"You ain't looked my way once in forty-eight hours," he said. "Is somethin' 'botherin' ya?"

"Well, if you must know, there is," I sulked.

"Is it somethin' I did?"

I looked away.

"I know," said Pop, "It's that money I won from ya at cards. I'll tell ya what, Sonny. Y'can have it all back. How's that?"

I laughed coldly. "Oh, it isn't something you've done. It's something you *haven't* done."

He scratched his chin. "Let's see now. What ain't I done?"

"You ain't told me nothin' about wet fly fishing," I said sarcastically. "Is it because you don't think I'm dry fly enough behind the ears yet to know?"

Relief showed on Pop's face. "Wet fly? I'll show ya, Sonny. Right now, if y'like."

"Goody-goody!" I cried, and ran for my waders.

Pop was in no hurry to get into the water. "My room-a-tism is actin' up again. Sometimes I'm sorry I didn' become a huntin' instead o' a fishin' guide. This standin' in th' water is fer th' birds."

He meant cranes, of course.

"Wet fly," he began, "is fishin' beneath th' surface o' th' water. It's fer when th' trout won't rise to a dry."

"I see."

"No, Sonny, in dry fly y' see—in wet fly, y' don't see. Th' wet fly fisherman hasta do a lot o' figgerin'—th' speed o' th' current, th' depth o' th' water, an' he's gotta use strad-agee."

Was there any sport that didn't require brains, besides shooting paper clips out of an office window?

"Now you been studyin' trout for a week. What've ya noticed?"

"That sometimes I can't catch them."

"Co-rect! an' th' reason ya can't catch 'em sometimes with a dry fly is because they jus' don't feel like surface feedin'. They're too busy foragin' nymphs an' strugglin' insects below."

Pop tested our fly rods. "One with soft action is good fer wet fly, but a medium action rod is good too because y'can cast either a dry fly or wet fly just by changin' th' fly on the leader connectin' to the' line. Fer wet fly we won't use th' automatic reel."

He fixed the manual reel to a nine-foot pole, selecting a long one because "the lake's so big. In a small stream seven feet'd be enough."

"A thin line is important in wet fly because it don't make too much disturbance in th' water," said Pop.

The one he picked tapered, he said, to six thousandths of an inch at the tippet.

"Some fishermen think a trout only goes for a fly th' second it hits th' water. But that ain't true," Pop pointed out. "They c'n wait."

"It's only etiquette," I said.

He walked into the stream dragging his leg, and said, "Now we gotta plan our attack."

I was ready for my assignment, no matter how dangerous it might be.

Pop stared at the water. "Whaddya notice, Sonny?"

I said, "Muddy water. Visibility zero."

"That's when wet fly comes in handy," said Pop. "In clear water we can throw a dry fly where we see th' fish. Now we gotta figger out where th' fish'll be. Know why they won't come up t' th' top? They're afraid o' two natural enemies. Ospreys—them birds—is one."

"What's the other?"

"Fishermen. Us. They're hidin' where they think we can't see 'em. Now, where's th' most likely place they'll go?"

I had no idea.

"Th' current," said Pop. "We gotta find th' current because that's where th' insects'll be, an' trout's bound to be where they can find food."

He paused to let me absorb what had been said so far, then continued: "The current is carryin' along th' insects that fell into it, so we gotta cast there, bein' careful not t' let the trout see our leader, or any shadows."

Pop made a few practice casts before letting his fly drop in the water about thirty yards away.

"Th' trick is t' let th' fly swim around on the surface fer a while, just like a real insect that wuz blown into the water, then let it sink," he said. "That's why a medium weight hook is better'n a heavy one that'd drag it right down."

"Very clever," I agreed.

"I always dapple th' fly lightly on th' water first, an' then draw it back a few times before lettin' it sink. That gets th' trout all excited."

"Why, you big tease!" I said.

"After doin' that a few times, all ya gotta do is let th' fly float downstream an' if any trout seen it before, they'll fight it out amongst themselves to get at it."

Pop dappled a while, then passed me his rod. "Me leg is killin' me," he complained, and limped out of the stream.

I watched him practically pole-vault into a hammock that had been among the many things the tackle shop sold me and surmised from previous experience what was going to happen.

"Lay that rod handle 'cross th' fingers, keepin' th' reel on bottom like yer shakin' hands with it," his voice called. "Now keep yer thumb on top an' start rotatin' th' wrist. Use yer left hand t' control th' amount o' line in th' air, or in th' water. Y'can also use it t' retrieve that wet fly."

My thoughts drifted. Could a man who broke the rules succeed as a fisherman?

I tried a few overhand casts.

"Keep it short, an' see that th' line is kept in slack. Move that arm like yer wavin' g'bye to your mother-in-law. Now practice a side arm cast in case ya run into a spot where there's too much overhead."

A breeze came out of the tideland spruces on the far side

"What did you say I was doing wrong?"

of the stream and gently swayed the hammock. It wouldn't be long now.

"Flex yer wrist t' th' rear . . . Sweep yer rod back . . . Shove it forward . . . Play out some line . . . Slope yer upper arm down . . . Lift that line offa th' ground . . . Slowly raise th' rod . . . Begin th' forward cast soon as th' line straightens out behind ya . . . Release the slack line . . . Let it pull through them guides . . ."

The voice faded away.

I knotted a tiny fur-and-feather wet fly and made some short casts with it along the bank of cottonwoods. When the fly disappeared beneath the surface, I imagined some trout giving it the once over.

Today I am a man, I said to myself. Today I am a wet fly fisherman and a dry fly fisherman. Oh yes, today I am a man!

I repeated my cast over and over again, making short ones and long ones. All was still in the hammock now. What a thrill it would be to give a yell of excitement and yank something out of the water, just to startle its slumbering occupant, I thought sadistically.

Alas, I had no cause for such a prank. There was no bite. Was I throwing a shadow where I stood? Could the wary trout see my waders and tell a man was standing in them?

I changed my base, shifting to a small island from which I made repeated casts into the main current. When there was a drag, I tried shorter casts, thinking this would make the fly more appetizing. No takers.

I tried a Quill Gordon and a few other kinds of wet flies,

but the trout passed them up—if there were any down there at all.

When would the great unseen drama take place? When would my fly be mistaken for a swimming nymph or hatching insect struggling upward to freedom, and an unsuspecting trout take it?

Further downstream, my next base, I found a nice spot, but there was such a preponderance of sunken logs and rocks that I left in a hurry.

I finally chose a large, craggy boulder and hid behind it like this was a game of cops and robbers being played, except that cops and robbers don't bother casting flies into one pocket of water after another, taking care that their leaders fall softly, and that their flies float free of drag.

The stage was now set. But only one of the performers was present. Me. Where was my co-star, Tallulah Trout? *Any* trout?

The house lights dimmed. So did my ambition.

I tried other flies. Other hooks.

Once I had a nibble, but nothing came of it.

Finally I kicked the water savagely and walked out, back to camp.

Pop was peering into the gloom, looking for me.

"Double trouble," I said, despondently. "No luck with a wet fly, no luck with a dry fly. It can only mean one thing."

"What's that, Sonny?"

"The damn fish are on a hunger strike."

Pop laughed. "Eat up an' we'll try again."

"It'll be dark by then."

"I didn't mind not catching those others, but this one looked up at me and said 'I dare you!' "

"Night fishin' beats all," he grinned.

We ate.

"Let's go," said Pop, picking up his rod.

I stayed close behind. We walked along for about five minutes.

"Shouldn't we be in the water by this time?" I asked.

There was no answer.

I repeated the question, louder.

There was a splash a short distance away. "The water's over here," Pop called.

I followed the sound of his voice until I was in the stream next to him.

"That's the toughest thing about night fishin'," Pop said. "Findin' th' water. Now, if I only wuzzn't so darn wet . . ."

He rejected my suggestion to go back and change. " 'Tain't necessary. I brung along some dryin' fluid fer jus' such an emergency."

I heard a cork pulled out of a bottle, and a swig of liquid being taken.

"Wanna sip?" Pop asked finally.

The smell of alcohol nearly knocked me over. "No, thanks," I said.

There was a gurgling sound again. "All right, bring on them trouts!" Pop shouted, his voice thickening.

My eyes were beginning to grow more accustomed to the darkness.

"Now, Sonny, we hafta depend on our ears," said Pop.

I listened, but all I could hear was the sound of the cork being pulled out of the bottle every minute.

"They're gonna start gettin' active any minute," said Pop.

"If you mean the mosquitoes," I said, swatting my wrist, "I got news for you. They're active already."

"Then take a sip o' this bug repellent," said Pop.

"I thought it was drying fluid," I reminded him, but the gurgling sound drowned out my words.

"After dark is when them hatchin' insects become active," said Pop. "See if y'can hear the surface o' th' water bein' broken. That'll be the trout grabbin' the nymphs as they're risin'."

I listened carefully for a few minutes and indeed did hear the sound of water being broken. I cast quickly in that direction, and waited to see what would happen.

There was a pull on my line!

"I think I got something!" I announced joyfully.

"Y'have," said Pop. "Ya got me by th' seat o' th' pants."

He unloosened my hook and took another snort. "It's gettin' cold, Sonny. Want some antifreeze?"

I checked my impulse to bawl him out. After all, if my guide wanted to get drunk, it was his business. But then again wasn't it also his business to be my guide? Or did he assume that people liked to be steered wrong?

My mind returned to the task at hand, night fishing. And again I began casting.

After a few hundred casts one's arm begins to feel like lead. "Night fishing is for the owls," I remarked, wearily.

Pop didn't answer. He was too busy gurgling.

Suddenly there was one big splash. I cast quickly whence the sound had come, crying: "What was that?"

"Th' bottle," said Pop. "I finished it."

I retrieved my line disgustedly.

"He finds the best places!"

"Wonder what I done with that can o' loom-in-us paint?" he said. "It's great stuff fer night fishin'."

You probably drank it, I wanted to say.

Suddenly Pop went into a crying jag. "Oh my poor brother Rob," he cried.

"I didn't know you had a brother," I said. "Was he a fisherman too?"

"Yep. But one day a fish got away from him. Rob claimed it wuz th' biggest fish in the world. He got so mad after that he turned against s'ciety. Started robbin' trophies from fishin' tournaments."

I waded around in the dark, listening for sucking sounds, and casting whenever I heard one. But if my fly came even close to the mark, I could not tell.

"Why don't they have radar for this?" I asked.

There was no answer from Pop.

Had he fallen over in a drunken stupor and drowned?

"Pop!" I shouted, chilled at the thought.

I called his name again and again, and kept on calling until I was hoarse. This was my fault. I should have watched out for Pop. He was such a lovable old fellow, in spite of being a hustler at cards, an inveterate liar, a braggart—and a tippler.

What was it Pop had said? Night fishermen must use their ears. I used mine and heard the sound of snoring a short distance away.

I stumbled around and finally found Pop flat on his face in the bushes, fast asleep.

"Wake up," I said, shaking him.

"Dolly, is that you?" he mumbled.

"No, it's me," I said.

"Durn the luck," he groaned, sitting up. "What're we doin' out here at this hour, Sonny?"

"We're fishing," I said. "Night fishing, to be exact."

He yawned. "That's ree-dic'-lus. Let's go t'shleep."

"You can, if you like," I said. "I happen to come from a long line of people who stick to a thing once they've started it."

"A good fisherman hasta know when t' put off 'til t'morrow what he couldn't catch t'day," said Pop.

"I thought a good fisherman never gives up," I reminded him.

He started staggering away.

"Can you make it by yourself?" I asked.

"I'm a guide," Pop said proudly, and flopped into the water.

I started to help him up but he shook me off and staggered away into the dark under his own power.

Why didn't I join Pop back in the tent, I wondered? What was I doing out here alone in a stream in the still of the night? How could I explain my presence to Boris Karloff if he came along?

Was this fisherman's fever? And if so, how far was it to the bughouse?

How long I stood there until my pound and a half denizen of the not-so-deep arrived on the scene to make the long, lonely vigil worthwhile, I do not know. It seemed like hours. Anyway, at long last—here he was.

By this time I was trained enough to wait the few seconds before setting my hook and then, like a fighter whose eyes are both closed and who goes on fighting only by instinct, I remembered what to do . . . "set the hook . . . not too sharp a jerk . . . watch that drag . . . just a lift of the wrist . . . forget the net . . . it's not time yet . . . he's heading for the logs and rocks . . . give him pressure . . . he's under them now . . . here he comes out the same way he went in . . . there he goes into a surface roll . . . relax your rod before he tears the hook out . . . hold your rod high . . . play him out . . . watch that lost line . . . okay, it's time for the net . . . get him in head first . . ."

Minutes later I was shaking Pop and showing him my trout.

"Night fishin's great," I said. "Only one thing—I don't know whether I caught this one with a wet fly or a dry fly."

13

IT SEEMED I had just closed my eyes when reveille sounded.

"Time fer breakfast," Pop said.

I turned over and hugged the covers, but it was no use. A man can sleep through bugles, drums, even crying brats—but once the smell of frying bacon reaches his nose, good-bye Morpheus.

"Oh, well," I said, rolling out of my sleeping bag, "Edison got along on only an hour's sleep, too."

"Where'd he fish?" asked Pop.

I didn't answer. It would mean having to explain about electricity, motion pictures, the phonograph . . .

"What am I going to be today—dry fly or wet fly?" I asked, feeling positively schizophrenic.

"Whatever th' sit-yee-ation calls fer," said Pop, ladling out the food. We dined hurriedly and got down to the stream.

A fast current was sweeping past the big boulder. "That's a dandy spot," said Pop. "Th' insects are blowin' against the rock an' fallin' in the water."

"How ghastly," I said.

"Know what they do then?" Pop asked.

"What can anybody do with his brains dashed out?"

"They sink, an' then rise again. So we gotta dapple our fly."

I watched Pop dapple. Then he falsecast a few times to dry the fly off, and let it float downstream. The technique was so clever I would have grabbed the fly myself, if I were a trout. Indeed, one did go for it, as I was tying a small Black Gnat on my own hook, and Pop pulled him in.

A good position, I decided, was on the other side of the boulder. I went there but my line got snagged on some overhead the first cast I tried.

"You're improvin'," said Pop, while I was freeing my line.

"How do you figure that?" I asked.

"Ya didn't curse then," he pointed out.

Had I been guilty of using foul language? I hung my head in shame.

Pop suggested I try a side-arm cast. "Shoot it out horizontal," he said, gesturing the way it should be done.

I tried, keeping my line parallel with the ground as I swung it around. But as I started the backward sweep, Pop let out a yell.

"Sorry, Sonny," he said, "I got him first."

I was hooked into the trout he had just caught!

Pop scaled the fish with a dexterity I couldn't help envying. I'd do mine—if I caught one—when he wasn't looking, I decided.

I had no luck for several hours and was glad that my rod was an all purpose one, allowing me to switch from dry to wet fly.

My overhand and even side-arm casts were now becom-

"Interesting cuss words Hogan uses. I've never heard half of them!"

ing graceful and fluid, and even if I wasn't getting fish, I was getting something else—exercise.

"Strike!" I called, whenever my fly hit a target in the water.

"Ball!" I called when I missed.

I struck out sixteen men and gave up eight bases on balls.

"How ya doin'?" Pop shouted, a hundred yards away.

"It's tie score in the ninth inning," I answered.

He scratched his head and probably considered coming over to take me out of the sun.

Before I could finish my little game of make-believe, I saw something—a swirl of color right near my fly—a trout was inspecting it. I held my breath.

"Please, God," I whispered, "Let this be it. I've been a good boy."

I let the fly float along a few feet and then—there was a strike, but this time a real one!

"Hoo-ray!" I shouted.

I played my trout out, turning him away from a mass of driftwood, and carefully steered him downstream.

"Hold yer rod high," Pop shouted. Then he shut up, curious to see what I could do on my own.

I got my trout away from behind a sunken log, and soon had him about a rod's length away. Then I started using the net. But it wasn't all over. He suddenly started going again. Now I had to steer him away from a log that he started for with diabolical cunning, probably figuring I would snag my line. But in a few minutes I had him within reach of my net once more.

Again I thought the fight was out of him. Again my think-

"Not quite. You're just supposed to remove the scales."

ing was all wrong. Every time I reached for him, he jumped away, thrashing the water furiously and churning it like a mangler.

An area yards around grew white with his splashing, and my net missing, and on shore I could hear Pop laughing as though he were watching an old Buster Keaton movie.

Finally, with a last desperate swing of my net, I had my trout.

"You little son-of-a-gun," I said. "If you want to live so much, who am I to stop you?"

I pulled the hook out and let him go.

14

WE STAYED at this primitive outpost for five days and I grew more and more proficient with my fly rod. I also grew bronzed and lean—bronzed from the sun and lean from the absence of a refrigerator to run to for a cold beer whenever I wanted one, or my customary midnight snack.

There were times when hardships like this became unbearable. But whenever I felt myself weakening, I heard the voices of my friends back home, jeering: "They laughed when he sat down at the Pole—North, that is," and I determined to go on.

"Is there anything you miss, Sonny?" Pop asked, as if he noticed the struggle going on inside me. "Anything at all?"

"No, I came up here to rough it," I said, firmly.

He asked the question several times. Each time my answer was the same.

Without Pop around, of course, I could not have gone on. And when he began disappearing on mysterious junkets, I became deeply disturbed.

To keep him by my side I began volunteering for those gin rummy games, although I knew it was in the cards—I'd wind up losing.

I lost about $600 in the five days.

Still Pop kept disappearing.

Where was he going?

I decided not to take my eyes off him for a second. I watched him when he fished, I watched him when he went into the tent for his periodic naps, I watched him when he excused himself to go into the woods for a minute. . . .

And then he was off—going somewhere. I could see it in the furtive way he kept glancing over his shoulder.

I followed close behind, too worried lest I get lost in the brush to be concerned about the crackling sounds I made whenever I stepped on a twig or dry leaf. However, my woodsman friend up ahead was making twice as much noise, so he couldn't hear me.

What was the old reprobate up to? With every step of the treacherous trail my curiosity grew and grew.

At last he came to a signpost on a tree, and stopped. I watched closely.

Pop brushed the dust off his clothes, straightened his cap, and smiled mischievously. Then he went on.

I walked up to the sign and read it:

ONLY 500 YARDS AHEAD TO
KLONDIKE KATE'S
DRINKS AND REFRESHMENTS

I went back to the stream and fished.

When Pop came home I didn't say anything about where he had been. Instead, I said: "I'm disappointed."

"In what?" Pop asked, blushing.

"In these trout I've been catching. Frankly, I'm afraid my friends are not going to be impressed when I tell them how big they were."

"What'd they expect? Trout ain't as big as tuna."

"They won't understand that. To them fish are fish."

"Y' c'n do what most fishermen do," Pop said.

"What's that?"

"Lie."

He said it so calmly I was stunned. It was a point that had been bothering my sub-conscious. Was it true that fishermen are prone to exaggerate? Here was one of their leading protagonists admitting they did. They lied with their boots on!

I flushed. "Listen," I said, "maybe I could rob and steal, even embezzle a little. But lie? Never!"

"Fishermen don't lie because they like t'. They lie t' make people happy," said Pop.

"How do you figure that?"

"People like t' be told there's big fish, th' same way they like t' be told there's ghosts."

"I don't want to just *tell* my friends about a big fish, I want to be able to hit them over the head with one. You see —they laughed when I said I wanted to go in for fly casting."

Pop shrugged and went into the tent.

I got out my fly-tying kit and began working on a super-insect. When I was finished, I took my gear and went downstream.

"This is for doubting Thomases everywhere," I said, and went down to the stream.

As the afternoon wore on, I started casting, letting my fly go down with the current.

When I retrieved upstream, I jiggled the line like a strip

"I *still* don't believe you!"

teaser might. Was it sex, perhaps, that the big trout wanted? Well, here was a burlesque.

I waded slowly and silently upstream and downstream as the shadows gathered, letting the current have my streamer time and time again. And always when it came back to me, I jiggled that line the same sensual way.

About a half mile from camp it happened, starting merely with a faint premonition that something besides the current had hold of my streamer. Then with a loud noise my reel had never made before, the line suddenly started running, yards at a time!

I let go for a brief second, as per my training, then checked it. By the overwhelming pull, I knew I had a whopper. Could I handle such a fish?

Now it began—the mad running upstream and downstream, the hysterical praying that I would be able to stay clear of rocks and roots.

Just before reaching the end of my line, I turned him around and he came rushing back to me. I stripped for all I was worth. . . .

What was it Pop had said? I frantically started to recall: "Feed the line slowly, with your left hand . . . reel in the slack with your right hand . . . watch that mess of loose line . . . you might step on it . . . get that line stowed where it belongs . . . play him from the reel . . . strip again. . . ."

Then I realized I wasn't just recalling the words. Pop was on the bank, shouting them to me: "Wear him down . . . gentle pressure now . . . get him tired before you pick up that net . . . watch that last struggle, he may have one big surge left . . . now scoop . . . get him in head first. . . ."

At last it was over. I came out of the stream bathed in perspiration, and staggering under my trout.

Pop gaped.

"Biggest trout I ever saw," he said, finally.

I lay down on the ground to rest. "I think this calls for a celebration," I said.

"Sure, Sonny. I'll open up that can o' beans I been savin'."

"I mean a real celebration," I said.

"What kind d'ya have in mind?"

"Maybe there's a place around here."

He reddened. "What kinda place?"

"Oh, just a place with drinks and refreshments."

"Well, er—there's one a little distance from here." He coughed.

"Klondike Kate's?" I asked.

Pop looked shocked. "How'd you know?"

"I belong to the Diners' Club," I said.

"Well, what're we waitin' fer?" he grinned.

The next day we gathered up our things and returned to camp.

15

Now I LAY me down to sleep the final evening of my glorious fisherman's holiday in Alaska. The winds from the Pole—just a snowball's throw away—had heard I was leaving and came to kiss me farewell. They came through every chink in the floor, walls and ceiling of my shack, in gusts that almost tore the covers off me. It grew so cold, even with my hat and shoes on, that I got up and put on two extra suits of the heavy woolen underwear which my wife, God bless her, had packed for me. But it was no use. I just wasn't Admiral Peary.

I grabbed my flashlight and, wrapped in all the bedclothes I could grab, ran shivering out of my shack to Pop's, to beg for more blankets.

I pounded on his door. No answer. None, after trying again, and again and again.

The PRIVATE didn't mean a thing to me at a time like this. I burst in. Then—stopped short in amazement as a wave of hot air hit my face.

Was there a secret heating device in here? There must be, I decided, starting to perspire. It just couldn't be that I was flushed with excitement.

The floor, too, felt strange. I glanced down and, by the flashlight, saw that it was carpeted wall to wall!

I swept my light over to the corner where all the snoring was coming from and there in a four-poster bed, quite snug under a mountain of quilts, lay Pop, a beatific smile on his face.

On the wall behind him were pin-up pictures of Billie Dove, Mary Pickford, Lila Lee, and a few other screen stars of a bygone era.

I tiptoed out quietly and closed the door. Then I went back to my own shack and waited for gangrene to set in.

In the morning Pop came over while I was packing, to say goodbye. The old man had tears in his eyes. "Wind got in 'em," he said.

I felt sort of all choked up myself. "What are you going to do—stay here?" I asked.

"Sure, Sonny. What do polar bears do?"

"They go to a zoo in some warm city, if they're lucky," I said.

"Yeah, an' die of broken hearts," he retorted.

"Only if people don't throw them peanuts."

I was about to pack away a bunch of my flies, and turned to him with them. "Here, Pop. I want you to have these."

He studied them closely. "Sonny, y'sure learned fly-tyin' good. I'm proud I taught ya."

It had been a wonderful relationship. Very often, I knew, lifelong friendships come to a violent end when two people are alone under such conditions.

"And I'm proud that I studied with you, Pop."

We gripped hands and Pop was reluctant to let mine go.

"I'll see you next year," I said cheerily.

"If I'm around," Pop answered in a low, choked tone.

"Maybe they should have gotten to know each other before going on a two weeks' fishing trip!"

An Eskimo was waiting to take me down the river in a canoe. I took a last look at the little shed that had been my home for two weeks, brushed a mist from my eyes, and said, "Shove off."

I kept waving to Pop—he kept waving to me—until the Eskimo let out a holler. But it was too late. We were tipping over.

"Go home, damn Yankee," I heard the Eskimo say as he went down for the third time, but I pulled him out anyway.

A few minutes later I was drying off back at the shed.

"It must have been Fate," I told Pop. "There was a little idea I wanted to discuss with you. It would give me a business interest and provide you with plenty of pigeons for gin rummy."

We discussed the idea.

Then we drank to its success.

Once again there were the goodbyes. This time, no waving.

A few days and one meal aloft later I was back home rushing into my ever-loving wife's arms.

"Sweetie, you sure look good to me!" I panted.

"I wouldn't be surprised, after all those fish," she giggled.

Dora was so anxious to get me alone, there were only 450 people in our apartment. There probably would have been more if it weren't for the fire department ordinance against overcrowding. However, some of the guests even knew me.

At two o'clock in the morning my wife stood up on the piano, and hollered, "Friends, Syd would like your attention for a moment, please."

"Heck, he's going to show home movies," muttered a group, and left.

The others quieted down expecting something would be said pertaining to more food and drink.

"Like lots of sportsmen everywhere," I said, "you've probably all been eyeing the distant waters of our northernmost state."

"Thish crowd never looksh at water," a voice heckled, and everybody laughed.

"Well, I just bought part interest in a fishing camp up there," I announced.

Lillian Kropp, one of our closest friends, fainted dead away and her husband had to squirt a seltzer bottle on her to bring her around.

"It's just a small place," I went on, "standing beside a fast moving trout stream, with the scent of balsam and cottonwoods in the air, and a few towering mountain peaks right on the property. But it's the kind of place where you can have a few fishing buddies, three squares a day, and a good clean bunk after a hard day of fishing. Rates are moderate—forty-five dollars per week per person—and we provide the following items: one ten by twelve-foot tent for each two persons, cooking utensils, dishes, Coleman stove, white gasoline lamp, axe and saw. Reservations are limited—only twelve people, a lucky dozen at a time."

Angry whispering broke out. "I didn't come here to listen to a pack of commercials," somebody said, and another group departed.

Was I mad to go on? The primitiveness was what I had

loved, what I had thought I'd be willing to fight and even die for.

"Boats will be available, too," I continued, "a small motor being recommended, three horsepower—or five and one half, if nothing else is available. Lake water has been approved by the health authorities and I can assure you that there is utmost safety since a small smoke signal from any island will attract attention. This, however, is to be used only in extreme emergency."

Some wiseacre turned up the hi-fi, but I didn't stop.

"Picture a wild, tumbling stream, hundreds of miles from the nearest vestige of civilization, where over eighty per cent of your casts will connect with three to eight pound trout—and larger," I shouted. "Most types of tackle are suitable. Live bait is not necessary but worms and small spinners are considered ideal for speckled trout and walleyes. As for clothing, friends, each two persons can get by comfortably with ninety pounds of baggage, or forty-five pounds each.

"Ice is available at our own ice house to keep your fish fresh on the long journey home. You can catch your limit the day before your scheduled departure. Bring a cooler."

Even Mortimer Clark was leaving. I had felt certain he would go for this.

"There's a bright new world waiting for you when you go angling," I concluded. "From the arctic circle to the Alaskan panhandle it is a life of rugged adventure that never grows old or comes too early in a man's—or woman's—life. What matter that television, telephones, and

"En garde!"

washing machines aren't close at hand? As long as you've got a fly rod in your hand and a melody in your heart."

There was a tug on my coat sleeve. I looked around.

It was my wife. The room was empty.

"Anyway, you've got one recruit," she said.

"Who?"

"Me."

I took her in my arms. "It's unthinkable," I said gently. "No, don't try to say anything, dearest. Why, you've no idea what it's like up there. The hardships . . . the sacrifices . . ."

She put her finger to my lips. "Hush. I've been reading all about the land of midnight sun and grotesque totem poles," she said. "Today there is a brand new breed of adventurer—and adventuress—going to Alaska."

It was thrilling to hear Dora talk like that. Here was a facet of her I had forgotten existed.

"I've been thinking about it ever since you left," she glowed. "Miles of practically uncharted wilderness—586,400 square miles. I wouldn't be a wife if I didn't share it with you."

This was the girl I had fallen in love with, the freckle-faced kid whose books I had carried home from school—the only girl in my neighborhood who hadn't run when I threw stones at her but calmly stood her ground and threw one back at me, opening a hole in my skull that required fourteen stitches.

"But it's fraught with peril," I said. "Let me sleep on it and give you the answer in the morning."

"It's already settled. I've bought the clothes," Dora said,

swinging open her closet and revealing a dazzling selection of shorts, blouses, booties and sun suits.

She slipped into one outfit.

"That's for fishing?" I gasped.

"Don't you like it?"

"I do. I do," I said. "But I bet Vitus Bering never saw anything like it when he first set foot on the Alaskan mainland in 1741."

16

"ALASKA WELCOMES the sportsman," I said, as our canoe neared POP'S PLACE. It was the name we had finally settled on, out of hundreds—simple and concise. "Over a half million square miles of untrammeled woodland brimming over with lakes and streams beckoning to the angling enthusiast. Perhaps the greatest tribute of those who love game fishing is that they return to these cloistered waters year after year."

"I better take that down," said my wife, getting out a small notebook she generally uses for shopping lists and to jot down appointments with the beauty parlor. "It might fit in with the advertising we're planning for next year."

"You might also mention that the official bird of Alaska is the willow ptarmigan," I suggested.

"And that the forget-me-not is the state flower," she added, then grew pensive. "Do you think people would want to know, too, that the international date line runs through Bering Straits, and that when it's Monday on Little Diomede, it's Tuesday on Big Diomede?"

"People who write for fishing information want to know everything," I said.

Our Eskimo guide raised and lowered his oar silently, his face inscrutable. Did he resent our intrusion on the

"Did you tell anybody about the good catch we made here yesterday?"

land of his ancestors? Did he have an inkling of what the future held?

"Take this," I said. "Alaska has always been a mecca for anglers. Attention was first attracted to it by the writings of a journalist named Benson who came here for his health in the eighteenth century. Benson's articles in sporting journals of the day, extolling his fishing successes, created an avalanche of interest and in 1788 the Eskimo-American Guides Association was formed—the first body of its kind in the New World. Descendants of these original members whose names have become almost legendary in the annals of sport fishing, are still locally engaged as guides and outfitters and the yarns they spin help while away many pleasant hours at the campfire."

"Is that on the level?" Dora asked.

"I got it right from the grapevine," I said.

The Eskimo was pointing.

"There it is!" I shouted. "POP'S PLACE!"

For an instant there was a look of excruciating pain on my wife's face like the one she had the day the man said the chinchilla jacket in the window was only $14,500.

Then she smiled bravely, and said: "It doesn't look like much of a place, does it?"

"No," I agreed, "but I bet it will by the time a certain female gets through with it."

Pop had on his best pair of suspenders. "I'm pleased t' meetcha," he said, taking off his hat and bowing.

The son-of-a-gun had even combed his hair for the occasion!

"Darling," I said, "I want you to meet the nicest man over

seventy in the Arctic Circle. Only watch out for him. He carries a deadly weapon in his back pocket—a deck of cards."

"I'll be careful," promised my wife, rolling up her sleeves. "And now if you boys will step aside, there's work to be done."

So saying she began rushing around the place, straightening things, ordering an alteration here, a new addition there. . . .

Pop watched wide-eyed. Several times I saw him gulp when Dora threw out some beloved piece of junk, but he held his tongue and did nothing to hinder the progress.

While the work went on, I polished up the copy we'd use—if the ad agency approved:

EAST IS EAST AND WEST IS WEST BUT THERE'S NOTHING LIKE THE NORTH!

> Remember, at a fishing camp you don't have to dress formally. Blue jeans, sweaters, old boots or sneakers will do. Virtually no extra charges. At night you will enjoy singing songs of the old North. [I didn't know if there were any but figured if the old South had songs, so did the old North.]
>
> Everybody's friendly at a fishing camp. Gathered around a campfire under a yellow Alaska moon, you'll let the cares of daily living drift away. Frequently a square dance, or a fish fry, will close the evening and you'll sleep as you never slept before.

I read it to Pop.

"Y'sure this'll bring people fer me t' play gin with?" he asked.

"Not people," I said. "Pigeons."

At last the great job of reconstruction was finished. Alas, Dora looked that way, too. She sat very still, moving only to prepare our meals and tidy up after us.

"Mebbe she's worn out from all th' work," guessed Pop.

"I've never seen her like this," I said.

"In Fall sometimes y'see females at th' headwaters of a stream, brushin' away th' sand an' gravel with their tails, an' makin' a depression where they c'n deposit their eggs," said Pop.

"Hold on," I said. "Those are female trout you're talking about."

"Only kinda females I know," he said, and walked away.

I tried taking Dora for walks along the banks of the stream, pointing out the turbulent rapids and shallow, opaque pools. Here and there graceful falls sent up white foam with furious intensity and the prism of light unleashed a floodgate of colors.

"P.S.," she wrote at the end of an eight-page letter to Lillian Kropp, complaining about the ethics of Flo Warren at their last game of canasta. "There's a river here."

Would the inspirational beauty of the great forest that surrounded us send Dora flying for the oils and canvas she had brought along? They didn't, though there may have been others elsewhere dreaming of such a place.

In spite of all my efforts to arouse her from her lethargy, she went along the same way, quiet and brooding. One day I brought home one of my catches to show her. She looked at it with listless eyes.

"Know what it is?" I asked.

"Dead fish," she said.

"Just why do you keep making a motion to adjourn?"

"It's a speckled brook trout—*Salvelinus fontinalis*," I corrected her. "Notice the coloration. Which other of God's creatures is so finely marked with varying tints of gold, crimson and blue, and has such luster and sheen?"

"It's still a dead fish," she said.

Mid-summer weather was now upon us.

"Trout don't like hot sun beatin' on th' water," said Pop. "They'll be seekin' the cooler water upstream. Chances are we'll find 'em in the riffles."

The thought of Dora sitting back at camp, alone and disconsolate, made me nervous and when a trout took my fly, I struck too quickly, tearing the hook away from him.

After I committed the same blunder a few times, I went back to camp. Dora was shaking out a mop. I watched her like a movie talent scout.

"Wonderful!" I exclaimed.

She looked at me puzzled.

"The way you were shaking out that mop. Try doing it with this," I said, handing her my fly-rod and leading her out to a clearing.

"Hold it with your thumb extended along the upper surface of the handgrasp, and not bent around it," I said. "Get your wrist into the cast so you feel the rod bending to the top—just like you were giving the mop a shake."

Dora did, and was surprised when the line went sailing away.

"Try it again," I said, "and be careful that the rod does not go too far back, or the line will become dead in the rear."

She started to get interested in what she was doing.

"Don't start the backcast too easily," I said, wondering how much I sounded like Pop Jeeter. "Grasp the line with your left hand between the reel and the first guide. Paying out and retrieving is always done with the left hand—when you're a righty."

I explained as well as I could about side casts, wind casts, forward casts. At the end of an hour, Dora fell into my arms, exhausted but laughing.

"I haven't had so much fun since we learned those cha-cha steps!"

"You're adorable," I said, kissing her on the ear.

She glanced at her watch. "Oh, dear, I forgot about lunch!"

"Just open a can," I said. "Pop won't mind, and neither will I."

When Pop came back to camp, I said: "Mr. Jeeter, I'd like you to meet a fisherman."

He looked around. "Where?"

"Right here," I said, leading Dora out of the kitchen.

"Y'mean you wanna learn how t' fish?" Pop asked.

"I'd love to—if you'll teach me," my wife said, shyly.

Pop finished his lunch in eight minutes. "Before she c'n change her mind," he explained.

Dora ran into our shack which now looked like a little pink love nest. When she emerged a half hour later, Pop let out a wolf whistle.

I looked at him sharply.

"Sorry, Sonny," he apologized. "I never seen a fisherman like that."

"Mack Sennett designed all my wife's fishing outfits," I said.

Dora skipped down to the river's edge, and we followed her.

"Y'can fish from shore, or wade," said Pop.

"Wading sounds like fun but I'd hate to get these new booties all wet," said my wife.

"Besides, it's dangerous. Some of those rocks are slippery and who'd tie the tourniquet if you broke a leg?" I mimicked her.

"There's sev'ral diff'rent ways o' catchin' fish," Pop began. "Plugs, tie flies, worms . . ."

"How about dropping a hanky?" Dora asked.

Pop played dumb.

"That's how I caught him," she laughed, pointing to me.

"Worms make good bait," Pop said.

My wife shuddered. "I can't stand the thought of those gooshy things."

"It's hard work digging for them, too," I pointed out.

"A few o' them draped over a large hook behind a June bug spinner c'n produce results," said Pop, "but we don't regard worms as sportin'. Maybe they don't regard us that way either."

"What other bait is there?" asked Dora.

"Minnows is good," said Pop, "especially fatheads."

"Please leave my husband out of this."

"We're mostly interested in insects because fish eat 'em," said Pop, scooping up a grasshopper. "Watch close an' I'll show y'how t' bait this feller."

"Let him go!" screamed my wife.

"Grasshoppers are an enemy of man," I reminded her.

"You know how I feel about capital punishment," she said.

"Maybe 'y prefer cockroaches," suggested Pop.

"I certainly do not!"

"How about crickets? Trouts is fond o' them."

"How can anybody harm a cricket after that cute little Jiminy in Pinocchio?"

"Maybe trout never saw the picture," I said.

"I used t' raise bait fer profit," said Pop. "Had slugs, bloodworms, leeches, salamanders, flies, caterpillars, grubs, field mice, and dungworms."

"Didn't the neighbors complain?" asked Dora. "Where we live you can't even have a dog."

"Th' insects we use ain't real—they're artificial," said Pop. "Show her some, Sonny."

I showed my wife the store-made ones.

"It all began in Macedonia about 2000 years ago," I said. "An angler used hackle tips on his hook to imitate the natural fly and floated it on the Astraeus River, taking trout with much success."

Pop stared at me.

"I've been reading," I said.

"What are these cute little things made of?" asked my wife, examining the flies.

"Peacocks' tails, gray turkeys, and brown hens," I said. "Also dyed mallards, golden pheasants, et cetera, et cetera, et cetera. . . ."

"It's nice to see feathers coming back," said Dora.

"Hackle's best because y'can make a fly with it usin' only th' hook, an' some needle an' thread," Pop put in.

"That reminds me, dear," I said. "I've got some socks need mending."

"Since when do I mend socks?" she asked. "Why don't you just buy some new ones?"

"I'd hate to tell you how far the nearest store is, and the little toe of my left foot is awfully self-conscious," I pleaded.

"Here's how t' tie a fly with a deer-hair body," Pop said. "Looks hard, but it's quite simple."

He took a small bunch of deer-hair, held it up against the hook, pulled some turns of thread around it very tight, causing the hairs to stand straight out from the hook. Then he trimmed the hairs around with his scissors and fastened on wings and hackle.

"Y'can do th' same with caribou," he said.

"I can do the same with Syd's whiskers if he doesn't shave for a few days."

"There's hun'reds an' hun'reds o' variations o' flies," said Pop. "Anglers are always makin' new ones whenever th' occasion 'rises."

"Why can't they just have a set, like golf clubs?" asked my wife.

"Trouts' appetites keep changin'. I wuz out fishin' once with a feller an' he ain't takin' anything. 'What kinda fly y' usin'?' he keeps callin' over t'me. Finally, he comes over, grabs my rod, an' pulls up th' line. 'By God, it's a Hawthorne,' he says. 'I thought I told ya th' trout here won't take 'em!' "

Pop fixed Dora up with some gear.

"Now, both of you go away," she said, walking into the water.

We didn't move.

"Just leave me alone," she pleaded. "I'm too nervous with men watching."

Pop and I walked back to the shacks.

"How To Get Rid Of Your Wife For The Afternoon," I chuckled, and stretched out on the hammock for a nap.

"Sy-yd," came a call from the stream.

Pop looked up from a game of solitaire.

"She's hung up," he said.

I went down to the stream where Dora was, reeled in as much line as possible, broke her loose, and put on a new fly.

"I'll be all right now," she said.

I returned to the hammock. I was only half in, when the call came again.

"Same thing," said Pop.

"I thought you wanted to be left alone," I said, studying how her lure was caught, then pulling in the opposite direction.

When I got back to the hammock this time, Pop was in it. He just looked at me.

"I see what you mean," I said, and returned to the stream.

It was just as well that I did because my wife kept getting hung up all afternoon and I wouldn't have been able to take much of a nap anyway.

Why did men teach their wives how to fish? Did it make sense?

"Joe enjoys sneaking off once in a while for a little quiet fishing. I haven't heard from him now for three years."

That evening after saying goodnight to Pop, I went into our shack and there was Dora, with needle and thread.

"That's a sight that does my heart good," I said, proudly. "Did you get around to my socks yet?"

"Socks, my eye," she answered. "I'm tying flies."

The ones she had made didn't look bad to me.

They didn't look bad to Pop, either. He went running for his flit-gun, just like he had done when he saw mine.

17

A DAY OR two later a couple checked in while I was downstream chasing a trout that refused to come back and fight like a man. They were Mr. and Mrs. Williams, from some Midwestern state.

"Do you always go with your husband on his fishing trips?" my wife asked.

"Oh, she's the fisherman of the family," said Mr. Williams. "I'm just a bird watcher myself."

"What have you caught lately, Mrs. Williams?" I asked, after the amenities.

"Rainbow!" she burst out with enthusiasm. "Some real leapers. There was one that had just deserted the shallow waters and I found him at the confluence of two streams, where a couple of currents were joined. I hooked after a running fight downstream about seventy-five yards from where we started, and finally netted him. Used a Beaverkill."

Pop studied her admiringly.

"Stalking a fish and then his ultimate capture," said Mrs. Williams. "That's the supreme thrill."

"I'm a fisherman, too," said Dora, who had yet to make her first catch.

"Is that what those clothes are for?" asked Mrs. Williams.

"I was wondering. Personally, I'd be afraid without shoulder straps. This outfit of mine I've been wearing since I caught my first lunker!"

"The one thing I don't like is getting my hair blown apart," said Dora. "That stream gets awfully windy."

"Just leave in your pin curls, dearie," said Mrs. Williams.

"Perhaps Mrs. Hoff would rather join me in pursuing a scarlet tanager," said Mr. Williams slyly, appraising Dora's figure.

"I think she'd rather join me," said Mrs. Williams, giving her mate a withering glance and starting for the stream.

"I'd be delighted," smiled Dora, taking her fly rod.

Pop and I watched them go wading off together, around the bend.

I began to grow nervous.

"I'll be right back," I told Pop. "That woman might say something nasty to Dora."

I tiptoed along the bank until I could hear them.

"I always kill my fish immediately after taking him off the hook," Mrs. Williams was saying. "I simply insert my forefingers and thumb in his mouth and bend his head backwards."

Pop looked at me when I got back.

"What wuz they sayin'?" he asked.

"Just girl talk," I said, and started a game of gin with him.

As usual he ran ahead and was into me for about twenty bucks when there came a scream from where I had left the girls.

"It's Dora," I said. "She always sounds like that whenever I want to go bowling nights."

"Is my nose shiny?"

"Ain't y'gonna go see?" Pop asked.

"Sure, right after I knock, which I'm doing now," I said.

I got back eight of my dollars and dashed back downstream.

My wife was in a state of shock, unable to talk.

"The poor kid," Mrs. Williams said. "It was terrible."

"What happened?" I asked.

"Her very first cast the fly fell in the water and a trout sucked it in. Then came the fireworks. He started making gigantic leaps. You could see him clear as day—a male rainbow, about five pounds. Your wife played him into the shallows just like an old timer, and I passed her the net. Then just as she had that trout halfway in, he jumped out and got away."

"You poor kid," I said, putting my arm around Dora. "But you mustn't fret over a fish that got away. There'll be others."

"W-who c-cares ab-bout the fish?" she sobbed. "I just remembered that I forgot to stop the milk delivery back home!"

Mrs. Williams stepped between us. There's a time when women can give comfort to each other and men are just in the way. "All men are beasts," she said.

To my amazement, Dora nodded her head in agreement.

"In the first place, your husband should have provided you with a spinner. A girl can learn to use a fly-rod just as well as a man, but the rudiments of spinning are much simpler for a beginner."

"Just what I was thinking," said Pop, coming over. "An'

I'd like Mrs. Hoff t'have this spinning rod, which has long been one o' my fav'rites, fer th' nice job she done fixin' up this fishin' camp."

He handed Dora an ancient-looking rod with a long cork grip, and a reel whose spool faced the tip, rather than the side. From the line's end, a tiny spinner dangled.

"Oh, you shouldn't have!" said my wife, as though she had been presented with a set of cultured pearls. "I don't deserve such a lovely gift. Besides, how do I catch fish with it?"

"With a spinning rod y'can send your line as fer as y' want," Pop said. "It's great when th' river is fast an' th' fish are on bottom where a fly can't go. I'll show ya."

He took the rod and with a mere flip of his wrist, sent the line out about two hundred feet. "Now, as that lure sinks an' swings downstream, some trout'll flash out t' take it," Pop said.

The words were prophetic. A trout did come flashing out but Pop jerked his line away sharply.

"Not now when I'm teachin'!" he yelled, as though telling the trout he'd see him later.

"I love spinning," said Mrs. Williams, "except, of course, when there's a hatch on the stream. Then give me my good old fly rod."

"Are you sure this is a sporting way of catching them?" Dora asked, taking back the rod.

They assured her it was.

"And you can cast bait of all types with it," said Mrs. Williams. "Flies, nymphs, plugs . . ."

“ ’Course, the treble hooks ain’t sportin’,” said Pop.

“Even in the field of plugs, they’re stepping aside to single hooks,” Mrs. Williams pointed out.

“Th’ beauty o’ spinners,” Pop said, “is that backlashes are practic’lly impossible, an’ y’can learn in just a few minutes.”

“Then what am I waiting for?” laughed Dora. “Here goes!”

Let other men have wives who resented their pleasures. I was willing to share mine with my mate.

The smile on her face died as she cast off into a hopeless snarl of wiry coils.

“Blast it,” said Pop. “That gear never acted that way with me!”

He took the rod and reel from my wife and tried to straighten it out for her, but she stalked out of the stream in high dudgeon.

“Come back,” I shouted. “Spinning presents no problem that cannot be remedied simply.”

It was something I remembered reading somewhere.

“Let her go,” said Mrs. Williams. “A girl just has to have a good cry sometimes. Tell me, how old is she?”

“What has that to do with it, may I ask?”

“I don’t know. Menopause, perhaps.”

“I disagree. It’s just an acute case of lack of trout,” I said. “All my wife wanted to do was catch one.”

“An’ she will,” said Pop. “She will, with this very same spinner. It’s very simple. I’m gonna teach her advantages o’ cross-windin’ th’ line, how t’ handle an anti-reverse lock, gear ratio, how t’ avoid snubbing a line or fouling it, how t’

"Just think of me as the one that got away!"

splice 'em—multifilament or monofilament, what t' do about slicin' lines, avoidin' line twists, removin' wiriness, an' how t' tie knots—perfection knots, loop knots, barrel knots, clinch knots an' turtle knots."

I paled. Would Dora be able to stand up under it?

"She was only an English major at school," I said.

"I'm also gonna teach her about plugs," Pop went on. "Barricuda Super Midget, Tulsa Bee, Heddon Tiny Runt, Phillips Weedless Popper, Pequea Quilby Minnow, Lily Bay Moosehead Minny, Longendyke Moth, Garcia Pecos Eelet, Weedless Popper . . ."

"How about spinners and wobblers? She'll have to learn about them, too," said Mrs. Williams. "Garcia Safir, Orvis Long Spoon, Trix Oreno, Seneca-Side Winder, Lyford Birdwing, Airex Preska Perch, St. Claire Tail-Lite, Rockland Flirt . . ."

"An' plugs," said Pop. "I like t' see a trout hit th' surface, so I like a surface plug."

"I like one that drives and darts underwater when it's being retrieved, myself," said Mrs. Williams. "Also, the kind that have propellers in front, and sink in deep water."

"I'll hafta explain a little about hookin' arrangements fer strip baits, weedless hooks, bumper lines and leaders, too," said Pop.

"Crimping. Don't forget crimping," added Mrs. Williams. "Worst thing in the world is to have a big one break off because a line has become weakened."

I left them discussing a few more salient features of spinning and went looking for my wife.

She wasn't in our shack. She wasn't in the immediate vicinity of camp either.

I ran through the brush looking for her. Wild branches tore at me as I called: "Dora! Dora! Where are you?"

In a little clearing where once I had stood just before dawn, practicing, I found her. She was holding a fly rod.

"Get your wrist into the cast," she was saying. "Be careful that the rod doesn't go too far back . . . pay out and retrieve with the left hand . . . don't start the back cast too easily. . . ."

"Baby," I said, putting my arm around her waist, "I'm so glad you're all right."

"I will be, if I ever get this backlash problem straightened out," she said.

There was a shout from down the river and we hurried to the bank. Pop joined us.

A caravan of canoes was approaching. Lillian Kropp and her husband Sam were in one of them.

"I brought our whole Mouse and Spouse Club," called Lil. "Wait 'til you see the chic fishing outfits we girls have."

I read a proclamation: "You are stockholders in one of Alaska's most valuable resources—its sport fish. Preserve, protect and use wisely this heritage that insures recreation and sustenance to you and your descendants."

"The hell with fishing," said Sam Kropp. "Anyone for gin?"

Pop Jeeter grinned.